By Timothy L. Templeton

with Lynda Rutledge Stephenson

MasterTrack International, Inc.
San Diego, California

The Referral of a Lifetime

Copyright ©1999 by Timothy L. Templeton

Requests for information should be addressed to:

MasterTrack International, 12267 Crosthwaite Circle, San Diego, CA 92064

Library of Congress Cataloging-in-Publication Data
Templeton, Timothy L.
    The referral of a lifetime / by Timothy L.
Timothy ; with Lynda Rutledge Stephenson. -- 1st
ed.
    p. cm.
    LCCN: 98-92203
    ISBN: 0-9667845-1-0

    1. Selling--Fiction. 2. Success in business--
Fiction. 3. Database management--Fiction.   I.
Title.

PS3570.E635R44 1999   813'.54
                      QBI98-1616

Cover and interior design by Paul Lewis
Printed in the United States of America

99 00 01 02 03 04 05 06 /❖ RRD/ 10 9 8 7 6 5 4 3 2 1

This book re-re-inforces the truth I've
known: That relationships are more
important than whatever products or services
you sell.

Acknowledgements

(& the referral request on P90)

In appreciation of the author's relationships
and their influences on him that are represented
throughout this book, I dedicate this book to...

...my greatest champion and defender, my
wife Maria;

...to daughters Sara, Sheila and Susie, whose
love and presence in my life make me rich and
successful beyond my aspirations;

...Lynda Rutledge Stephenson, whose wonderful
writing and creative communication gifts make
this book an enjoyable read;

...Milt Richards, for his steadfast support and his
intuitive ability to identify the importance I place on
relationships and explaining their eternal meaning;

....Jim Green, for his humor and insights, not
the least of which included explaining the mantle
and detailing its meaning;

....Thom Black, for his insight and extraordinary
ability to reduce volumes into one meaningful
sentence;

....Paul Lewis, who continually delivers and
makes me look like a hero through our visual
brands and who coined "Just Let me Know!"
(among others);

...Dr. Ron Jenson, who upon my request encouraged me to "have at" the phrase high ground, a name under which he developed a meaningful ministry;

....Kerry McQuade, a faithful jogging partner and astute financial business consultant and CPA;

...Ron Cotrell, whom I've had the privilege of personally coaching through this system, and who first coined "demonstrated consistency" during our weekly coaching sessions;

... Brian Buffini, for the season we built Providence Seminars together and the many influences of the material in this book;

...Dwight Johnson, a dedicated advocate, who has embodied "demonstrated consistency" in his follow-through in the care of others;

...Dan Lickel, for making my personal Keep-InTouch program real;

...my father and mother, who consistently demonstrated God's love to me;

...my sister Beverly and my brothers Dave and Bob whom I love;

...Pauly Fuzak, who has been a best friend since childhood and truly understands the meaning of a lifetime relationship;

...to a dear friend, partner and mentor who first represented "Mr. Highground" in my life, Paul Wong.

"The concepts contained in *The Referral of a Lifetime* will transform not only your business but your entire outlook; indeed, these concepts can be applied even before you finish reading the book. I have no doubt you will recognize yourself in one or more of the main characters of the story."

—**Ron Cottrell**, Agent Re/max United

"This book will speak to those who understand that the greatest gift we give to someone is friendship, and that the best thing we can do to follow up a referral is to build a relationship with that person. Referral of a Lifetime will take you from referral to relationship, and possibly to a lifetime friendship."

—**Jim Green**, President
Akica-Great Western

"As an entrepreneur, the last thing I want to look like is an opportunist or pushy. The system outlined in this tale gives you the ability to draw people to you like a magnet without overwhelming them."

—**Richard Davies**, President
Fleet Card Fuels

"Telling someone I will treat a referral the same way I have treated him is a terrific stimulus to me to treat that first person correctly. It constantly makes me think through what I am doing with my current customers. *The Referral of Lifetime* is a practical guide for anyone who is in need of a specific program to build a profitable, enjoyable business for life."

—**Paul Goodman**, President
Floral Finance

"This is such an important book . . . it gives you the ability to identify your strengths, match them to a plan and win big in the marketplace."

—**Tom Challan**, President
First Priorities

"A thoughtful, well-written book outlining the power of relationships in sales. You'll be hard-pressed to find a better guide to help you to build a system in your business that will equal the results."

—**Keith Hentschel**, President
KLH Associates

"Insightful, simple, and filled with practical advice for anyone who wants to be successful in business."

—**Robert K. Butterfield**
Attorney at Law

"The Referral of a Lifetime is an unusual business book. It is unconventional thinking to value a long-term relationship over the short-term profits of your products and services. This book gives you a deeper appreciation of how to build a business in which you will never be considered a 'pushy' salesperson.

—**Craig Case**, Vice-President,
Sales and Marketing
Excel Nutraceuticals

"With clarity and purpose *The Referral of a Lifetime* articulates the power and benefits of investing in relationships. Its principles provide sage advice and timely guidance needed by compassionate professionals throughout the marketplace today."

—**Jeff Frichner**
Director of Business Development
Enable Incorporated

"If you never want to make a cold call again, this book is for you. And if you want to start enjoying your customers and retain them . . . read this book."

—**Robert and Melissa McCrea**
Impact Designs

Contents

About the Author

Timothy L. Templeton is Chairman and CEO of Mastertrack International Inc., a training and specialty publishing organization based in San Diego, California. Mastertrack specializes in training, supporting, and coaching corporate and independent trainers as well as individuals and companies in the principles and system outlined in this book.

Through his companies and years of experience in the marketplace, Tim has trained and coached thousands to a higher level in their business and personal lives by applying his core principle that the lifetime value of a relationship is more important than the short term profits of products and services.

Tim resides in Escondido, California, with his wife Maria and daughters Sara, Sheila and Susie. Tim may be reached at 1.877.321.6500 or e-mail at mastrtrack@aol.com.

with...

Lynda Rutledge Stephenson is a professional writer. Her work has appeared in major newspapers and magazines, nationally and internationally, and she has written 14 books in collaboration with others as well as two of her own.

Preface

A fter almost 25 years of marketing and selling products and services throughout the country, I have learned that certain things carry extreme importance, no matter the industry.

The overriding truth of all our work is that in the end, the relationships you've developed— what your associates, friends, and family think about you based on your actions and how you responded in all situations—are more important than the short term profits of your products and services. What you think about yourself based on what you truly think your God thinks about you is the true bottom line.

This book is about that overriding truth. Each character you meet from the very first page carries a message in this training. The story is written in allegory form representing the situations and emotions all of us who call ourselves salespeople, entrepreneurs or business people

11

have experienced at one time or another.

While you will learn how to build a business largely by referral;

While you will learn how to create lifelong loyalty with existing clients so that being replaced by competitors will be extremely difficult;

While you will learn a simple system that shows how to be pulled into sales rather than continually pushing, having your clients buy from you instead of having always to sell to them;

While you learn how to provide awesome customer service and create outstanding teamwork; there is more.

This book is about understanding a system that will allow you to enjoy who you are and to build your identity in the marketplace around that identity.

It is about knowing true success by being yourself every day.

❖   ❖   ❖   ❖

Chapter 1

I T'S ANOTHER PERFECT MORNING AT THE CALIFORNIA Coffee Cafe and Bistro, the favorite spot for the locals of the tiny, upscale California coastal town of Rancho Benecia. The fog is floating in from the harbor across the street as the regulars zip in and out or stay to chat, enjoying the ambiance of the little cafe.

Chuck, the owner, is standing behind the antique oak bar that had been there when the town was a harbor for the 19th century great sailing ships and the place was a watering hole for the waterfront's sailors of the sea. Now, though, Chuck proudly labored between it and his fantastically gilded espresso machine for this watering hole of a different era and all the friends it has made him.

He takes a moment, glances around, and smiles. Four of his favorite regulars are here right now.

13

In the center of the cafe with her grande double mocha is Sheila Marie Deveroux, one of the most recognized realtors in town. Flamboyant to say the least, the eclectic woman, with her raven black hair, her bright outfits, and her happy way of talking with her hands, was hard to miss at her favorite table in the middle of the morning chaos. Chuck couldn't remember the last time he had seen her here alone. She always has someone with her, which of course Chuck likes since that means yet another coffee drinker, but he couldn't help but notice that whoever the current person was, Sheila Marie would be treating him or her like family, always. As she had always done with him.

"Chuck! A fill-up please!" Chuck turns his head to another of his regulars—Paul Kingston, a casually dressed, thirty-something good guy, holding out his empty vanilla latte. Paul, a fixture each morning in the corner booth, with his sports page and his own special coffee mug, is one of those trustworthy men who knows everybody and seems to know a little of everything, who loves spreading it around and who has found a home in network marketing. Chuck could not think of one bad thing he'd ever heard about Paul. Except that he was talking about cutting down on his latte consumption. And that made Chuck all but laugh since he'd just ordered another.

And out on the patio sits Sara Simpson, young Female Entrepreneur of the Year at age 24, holding

court. It is Tuesday. Every Tuesday and
Thursday, 8:30 a.m. sharp, this is where she
and eight of her top employees meet. A dynamo,
all business and proud of it, Sara loves to have
her early morning meetings with all her system
engineers in the warm California coastal air under
Chuck's umbrellas. "Double espressos all around,
Chuck!" is always her "good morning." And he'd
always make hers a triple, just to see if she
noticed.

And then there's Philip, striding in on his
expensive loafers, for his large cappuccino no
whip with a purposeful, time-to-get-the-day-
started wave. Philip, who just turned 40, had
somehow turned his networking ability and his
early years hustling securities on Wall Street into
being "the" guy to trust in Rancho Benecia for
your financial planning. Everybody knew it;
everybody trusted him and told their friends
about him. "The usual?" Chuck calls as Philip
comes toward him, saving Philip a few seconds.
Philip gives him his trademark thumbs-up and
bellies up to the old oak bar, popping the correct
change on the counter to wait until Chuck has
delivered his morning brew, which Chuck does in
record time.

As he watches Philip pivot and head purpose-
fully back out the door with a smiling salute to
the coffee "colonel," Chuck gazes over the scene,
hands on his hips, enjoying the sight. That's when

15

he noticed Susie standing alone at the bar, staring
at the circles she was making in her coffee with her
spoon. Her usual—hazelnut with steamed milk,
Chuck remembered, and moved her way.

"Hey there."

Susie momentarily looked up. "Hi, Chuck."

"How are you doing?"

"Fine," she answered, unconvincingly,
continuing to stare into her cup.

Chuck leaned closer. "Okay. Now. How are
you really doing?"

Susie didn't even look up this time. "Oh, you
don't really want to hear it, Chuck. But thanks for
asking." She began to rap her fingertips nervously
on the counter.

Chuck pulled a biscotti from the big glass jar at
his elbow, placed it on a paper doily, set the doily
on a little plate, and slid the plate right to her fingertips, bringing them to full rest—and bringing
Susie's eyes up to meet his.

"Yes," Chuck said. "I do."

Susie could see that he did. She gave Chuck
the smallest of smiles and said, "Well, okay. The
thing is, I can't deny any longer that I've come to
a crossroads."

"What kind of crossroads?"

"The business kind. I may have to admit to
myself that what I've wanted I'm not really going
to get. And I don't know what to do about it. I
wanted my own business so desperately. I wanted

to feel some purpose beyond a 9 to 5 job, wanted to work for a dream of my own instead of someone else's. You know?"

"Oh, yes." Chuck sighed, looking around. "I know."

"I wanted to make a living, not just a paycheck that could disappear at somebody else's whim. So I got up all my courage and all my savings and...well, I risked. I tried. But," she paused, fingering the biscotti, "it's not working. And I may have to give up." She shook her head. "I mean, I have to be the absolute worst at cold calls. I can't do them. I cannot."

"So don't."

Surprised, Susie looked up at that.

"It's more than about making money, isn't it?" Chuck agreed.

"Yes. Or it was supposed to be. But maybe I'm not cut out to do anything but just put in my hours and get by."

Chuck leaned against the counter behind him, crossed his arms, and studied Susie.

Finally, Susie couldn't stand it anymore. "What? What's wrong?"

Chuck grinned. "Less than you think. Susie, you don't know how familiar this all sounds. Look. I'm going to give you a phone number. You can use it or not. But if you do, well, let's just say that when I used it, and I met and listened to the man on the other end—" He

17

waved an arm around at the busy place: "—the rest is coffee history." He grabbed a napkin and a pen and scribbled a number, and slid it over to Susie.

"His name is David Michael Highground. A good friend of mine referred me to him years ago, and now I'm doing the same for you."

Susie looked apprehensive. She'd heard so many pitches, read so many books, and heard so many big ideas for making it "out there." How could she get excited about another one? She didn't think she had the energy for another letdown.

"No, Highground's system isn't like anything you've ever heard."

That definitely surprised Susie. "Are you a mind reader, too?"

"No, I just know exactly what you're thinking. It's just another pitch, right? But have you ever heard a pitch that talks about relationships? Or building a business doing the right things at the right times for all the right reasons? Trust me, David Michael Highground does not now nor ever will have dollar signs on his forehead!'" Chuck laughed. "Yet he's the most successful man I know. It's not about money. He has all the money he will ever need. It's about purpose and personal fulfillment. That's what floats his boat now." He nudged the napkin closer to her. "It's your call. Let me know what happens." And he moved down the bar to wait on a new customer.

Susie stared at the napkin, then at Chuck, then back at the napkin. Absently, she picked up the biscotti, dunked it a few times, and took a bite. Chuck got busy again and Susie's thoughts went bleak once more. She swallowed the last of her coffee, then picked up her belongings, turned to leave, and remembered the napkin.

To her surprise, she reached out and took it. And with a glance back at Chuck, she left.

❖ ❖ ❖ ❖

Inside her car, Susie picked up her cellular phone, then put it down, staring at the number scrawled on the coffee shop napkin. A rush of thoughts, not the least of which was the thought of her cellular phone bill at the end of the month, made her hesitate. Maybe she needed to admit to herself that her dream didn't fit who she was. She just didn't have the right personality. Or something.

But the things Chuck said...

Well, she sighed. She definitely needed help, that was for sure. And she had nothing to lose, that too was for sure. So she dialed the number

19

and pushed the send button.

"Yes?" The response was surprisingly warm.

"Hello," she responded, trying to hide the nervousness. "Yes, hello...my name is Susan McCumber. Is David Highground available?"

"This is he," the voice responded, still just as upbeat.

She paused, enjoying the warmth. She wasn't used to that sound from a stranger. She had spoken with far too many strangers who hated receiving cold calls as much as she hated making them. She took a calming breath. "Mr. Highground, I hope this isn't a bother. You see, Chuck at the coffee shop gave me your name, said I should talk to you, that you have helped him and thought you might help me."

She could almost hear his smile over the phone. "Ah, yes, Chuck. He's a good man. Any friend of his is a friend of mine. How might I help you?"

Susie realized she no longer felt nervous. To her surprise, she found herself telling him everything:

20

"Well, you see, I went into business for myself six months ago. But now I seem to have lost my momentum and I'm beginning to think the problem is me. What I mean to say is that I started out so well and the company I'm affiliated with is fantastic and the people are so helpful....and I really believe in what we're doing. But I'm not making it work somehow. I've gotten off track and I can't seem to get back on. I feel like...like...." She made herself say the word she had been dodging for weeks: "...a failure."

Susie couldn't believe she had just admitted this to a complete stranger. But the weeks of continuing to attend meetings with others in her affiliated company was increasingly frustrating. To be around so many successful people who treated her with respect and encouragement made her feel upbeat. But each week the vision of her actually attaining the same level of success seemed to decrease with her absolute inability to get and keep others involved in her program. In fact, the several contacts a day she had been forcing herself to make had dwindled lately to nothing more than thinking about making them. And her workday had begun to consist entirely of looking forward to the next meeting to get a new idea, maybe a new ad or a new tape that would save her. Day by day, she could actually feel her confidence draining away.

"Susie." Highground's warm voice snapped her out of her funk.

21

"Oh, I'm sorry," she said, embarrassed. "Really, forgive me. I just can't get my mind to stop thinking about it all."

"Susie—may I call you that?"

"Sure," she replied. "All my friends do."

"Susie, you're definitely not a failure,"

Highground began. "You're simply in a place that everyone passes through at some time in their career, and in life. You're on the mantel."

"The mantel?" she repeated. "You mean, like the shelf over a fireplace kind of mantel?"

Highground laughed. "That's the image. The mantel is a place to reflect. It's where the good stuff happens. It's the best place to be in for me to help you, because in order to get off the mantel and move forward permanently, you need a new plan. And you will move forward, I guarantee it. Does that make sense?"

"Absolutely," Susie responded.

"Okay, then," Highground continued, "before we meet I need you to know that my help is not for everyone. My philosophy or way of doing business doesn't match everyone, so before I agree to meet with you, I need to ask you a few questions. Is that okay?"

"Well," Susie said, "I suppose so. "

"All right. First question: Do you like yourself?"

Susie almost laughed. What a question.

Did she like herself?

She listened as Highground went on. "In other words, do you want to become more of yourself and refine the gifts you have been given instead of trying to imitate someone else?"

"I've never thought about it that way," Susie replied. "I can't say I'm 100% happy with my current situation, but as for myself, well, yes, I do like myself, basically."

"Very good," Highground said. "I didn't ask if you were happy with yourself. I help people become more of who they are, to become genuine. That's what others are attracted to."

Susie perked up. What a wonderful idea.

"So, question number two, Susie. Ready? Do you believe in your product and company? Are you proud to associate yourself with all aspects of the organization? It can't be only about making money. You see, I am going to show you how to build lifelong advocates of you and your company, so it's imperative you are absolutely sold out for it yourself. That way, even in the event you were to move on, everyone you do business with will feel that you moved them to a better spot with the products or service of your current organization."

"There's no doubt about that," Susie replied emphatically. "That was why I got involved with the company in the first place."

"Excellent," said Highground.

"Now, question number three," said Highground. "And this is probably the hardest one. Are you willing to 'stay the course?' Everyone is different so the system applies differently to each. The one key thing, though, that everyone must have is what I call 'demonstrated consistency.' You will see results immediately, but the real lasting effects, the kind that can build

23

you a business and a life, happen only when
you adapt this marketing system on a daily basis,
consistently for 120 days. Then it continues to build
and deepen each year thereafter. So the whole
system turns on this: Will you stay committed to a
course of action that won't include cold calling or
making others uncomfortable, but will take a daily
commitment on your part?"

Susie felt a bit overwhelmed. But there was
nothing that she was hearing that she did not
instantly like. "Well, yes. I'm ready to try," was her
determined response.

"Well, then, Susie, so am I," was his response.
"We'll meet this afternoon, around 3:00, at the
coffee shop, if that's convenient."

"Yes, I can be there."

"Good. See you then."

Before Susie could respond, Highground was
speaking again:

"Oh. One more thing."

"Yes?" she replied.

"You're going to do great."

Susie tapped her cell phone silent. What was
she getting herself into? But she trusted Chuck, and
this Mr. Highground seemed to be a good friend
of Chuck's. She caught a glimpse of herself in the
mirror. "And," she told herself, "you certainly have
nothing to lose."

She'd be there.

Chapter 2

A T 3 O'CLOCK SHARP, SHE WALKED IN TO CHUCK'S smiling greeting. He waved, held out a steaming cup of her usual, and nodded toward a table nearby. Susie took the cup and looked toward the direction of the nod.

There was a little table with a handmade "reserved" sign on it. Susie glanced left and then right, and seeing no one near, she strolled slowly over to it, and sat down.

"Hello."

Susie jumped. At her elbow stood a silver-haired, trim, nicely-dressed man.

"I didn't mean to startle you. I'm David Michael Highground."

She got up. "Oh, no, really, that's fine. I just didn't see you...," she mumbled at this mysterious Mr. Highground. She glanced back at Chuck who gave her a thumbs-up and rushed busily away, then she took a deep breath, and sat back down.

Highground's smile broadened and he waved at her chair. "Have a seat, Susie, and let's talk."

She sat and so did Highground. She took a sip of her coffee, suddenly more nervous and less trusting than she expected. Yet she kept thinking of Chuck and because she trusted him, she would keep an open mind.

Highground picked up on this, because the next thing he said was, "You're feeling hesitant, aren't you? I understand. It's the most natural thing in the world. But the reason I'm here is because a good friend of ours referred me to you, right?"

"Right," she answered, a bit embarrassed for being so transparent.

"Well, then, I have a responsibility to him to take care of you. Know why? No matter how great my business ideas might be, the relationship I have with Chuck is much more precious than any service or program. So I'll honor my relationship with him by helping you."

Sensing this was more than just a way to make her feel at ease, she said, "What do you mean?"

"I mean, this very dynamic we are acting out is the key to everything you will learn in the next two days. Let's turn it around. You value Chuck's friendship, don't you?"

"Yes, I do."

"Then if he asked you to do something in your power to do, wouldn't you want to do it and do it well?"

"Well, yes. I wouldn't want to disappoint him."

"Why?"

"Well," she thought, "because I value the relationship."

"That's it. That is the exact point. If you understand that your relationships are more important than your products or services, and you always put them first, the new people that come into your life will see this, realize you're the real thing by your actions, and will enjoy referring their friends and acquaintances to you, because they know you will treat their friends right when their friends need your services or products. Want an analogy?"

"Sure."

"Think of the world as a chicken coop. We can go searching for customers like they were chickens, running around trying to sell our products to every chicken we can corner. If we catch one, then we can have a good chicken dinner that night. But if we build a relationship with those chickens, take care of them, plump them up, we'll have omelets for life."

"Well, that's vivid," Susie said, with a grin. "Even if I don't like omelets."

Highground laughed. "Of course, I do like omelets, but you get the point, I hope." Highground sat back in his chair. "It's amazingly simple-sounding, I know. Not what we usually hear in business, is it? Most programs are hit and run. Hit 'em with our pitch, run to find the next customer to pitch again. Think about it. Most major companies have powerful marketing programs planned months, even a year in advance. But they focus on the product to the exclusion of the person buying it. And how much time is spent considering the type of person you happen to be and how that helps or hurts you in the program? None. Sound right?"

Susie thought about the seminars and lectures and meetings she'd attended. Everything was sell, sell, sell. Market, market, market. The client was a customer. And the question was always, how do you find the customers? "Yes," she had to agree, "I'm afraid you're right."

"But what happens when you flip that idea?" Highground said, flipping a wrist in a full circle. "The client first, then the product or service! Let me put this another way: I want to serve you well because of my relationship with Chuck. Tell me the truth. Would you have come here if we did not have a mutual friend?"

"No," she admitted, taking a sip of coffee. "Probably not. No offense."

"So, you are here, entrusting your time with me because of your relationship with Chuck. And if Chuck didn't value both of us, would we be sitting here?"

"No, we wouldn't," she said. "Relationships.

That is great, but how can that work in the long run? Surely it's too good to be true."

Highground smiled as if he'd heard that before. "What you are experiencing right now is the foundation you can build a business and a life on. And that goes for new clients and existing ones. Ready to begin?"

Susie nodded slightly, still a little stand-offish.

"You'll see," he said. "Just wait." And then Highground pushed a small notebook across the table toward her. "This little notebook is your 'working ground' for the next two days. And afterward, it will be your plan of action, all you have learned and all you need to know."

Setting down her coffee, Susie accidentally jostled some coffee onto the new notebook.

"Oh, no!" she gasped, wiping frantically with her napkin.

Highground joined in and in a second they were both laughing.

"I'm sorry," Susie said.

"Are you kidding? What better baptism for your new business life—Chuck's coffee!"

"Hey, keep it down over there!" a voice called from the front door. Highground looked back and waved. "Ah, there's one of the people you'll meet now! Sheila Marie! How are you doing?"

Sheila Marie waved her response, turning quickly back to the couple with her, steering them to her favorite table.

"Susie, in the next two days, you are going to meet four very different people who have been exactly where you are, and that woman is one of them."

Susie looked around. "Why, yes, I recognize her. She's as much a regular here as I am."

"And there's another." Highground pointed to Paul who was standing at the counter, paying for his coffee to go.

Somewhat surprised, Susie said, "Why yes. I know these people."

"Think about it. Is that so surprising? You know Chuck. They know Chuck. And so does Philip and Sara, who are the other two. I bet you'll recognize them, too. And of course, they know Chuck, too. We all know an amazing amount of people who know an even more amazing amount of people. Yet they were all exactly where you are right now, not too long ago."

"They were all like me? I find that very hard to believe. They look so...successful."

Highground paused, then said in his teacher's voice: "Do you think you have to be like them to be successful?"

"Why do I get the feeling that's a trick question?" Susie said.

"Remember the first question I asked you?"

"Yes: 'Do I like myself?' It was a very interesting question."

Highground nodded. "I have learned a very

basic but important truth over the years of teaching this system. You cannot and should not change anyone. You can modify some behavior habits, and fill in a gap or two, but not for long. We are all gifted in certain areas and we need to be more of ourselves, not less. Do you see Sheila Marie over there? Do you know what was holding her back? She is what I call a 'Relational/ Relational' person, and she was killing herself trying to be a 'Business/Business' person because she thought that's what she had to be to make a living in her profession."

"Relational/Relational? Business/Business?"

"Okay, let me back up. I believe we all see business and relationships through four 'windows.' Others see us and our style through the same windows. When we are not ourselves, when we try to be someone else, no matter how we try to disguise it, we feel uncomfortable. So our clients cannot help but feel uncomfortable too."

Susie frowned. "Did you say four 'windows?' What are the other two?"

"Okay, let's go through all four. You know the person who is always ready with a hug? He or she is Relational/Relational. In the middle are Relational/Business and Business/Relational. At the other end is Business/Business, the type who is only interested in the bottom line."

"What am I?"

That made Highground grin. "That's what you have to decide. In fact, over the next two days you will not only decide which you are, but you'll learn how to embrace it and apply it to your work."

"So, I get to be myself and I get to work with people who know someone I know?"

"Right."

"And the reason it works is because it's putting people first? Relationships are valued over the bottom line. And that, strangely enough, will allow the bottom line to take care of itself?"

"With a little more help from you, of course, which you'll soon learn, too. But yes, you're getting the idea."

Susie opened her notebook. Inside were four sections, each one with a picture of a combination lock at the top under the words: "The Right Combination for Success." She thumbed through the pages, then looked up. "Don't take this wrong, Mr. Highground, but it seems too simple. Why doesn't everyone do it?"

"You know that old saying that the trees are in the way of seeing the forest? Most people are too busy ducking the falling trees in business every day to think about the simplicity and rewards of just treating people right and doing the right thing. But this works—because it's built around you. And while it seems simple at the top, it's very deep below. Remember the third question I asked you?"

Susie quickly thought. "Let's see: 'Are you willing to stay the course?'"

"This is where the simplicity either works or it doesn't. I'm not selling magic, Susie. My system works because it's based on truths that, when applied, give back significant results. That last part is why I asked you if you were a 'stay the course' sort of person. And this is where I begin to introduce you to the people who have lived it and want to share it with you." Highground pointed to the notebook. "Read the first principle, why don't you?"

The cartoon picture of the combination lock had a pointer arrow, pointing to the first number: #1. And under it were these words which Susie read aloud:

"PRINCIPLE #1 **The 250x250 Rule.** It's not who you know, it's who your clients know that is important."

She looked up at Highground.

Highground leaned forward. "Tomorrow morning, you'll meet Sheila Marie. And that's what she'll teach you. Read on."

33

Susie turned the page. There was the same picture of a combination lock, but the tumbler lock had moved to show #2 at the top under the pointer arrow, as if the tumbler had turned. She read the sentence below it.

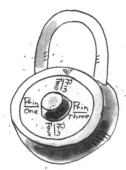

"*PRINCIPLE #2*   Build a database and ABC it."

"That will be Paul," said Highground. "We'll meet him for lunch, and he'll explain that." Highground pointed at the notebook again. "Okay, now. Principle #3."

Susie turned the page again. There was the same picture of the combination lock, but the tumbler had moved again to show #3 at the top under the pointer arrow. She read:

"*PRINCIPLE #3* 'Just Let Me Know'—Educate your clients through what you say and what you send them on a consistent basis."

Susie looked a bit confused.

Highground noticed. "Don't worry. You'll understand it all very soon. Philip will be explaining that principle and he is a whiz at it. Okay, read the last principle. That'll be Sara, and she's also amazing."

Susie turned the page.

The lock's top pointer arrow was now pointing to #4, and the lock was open. For some reason, she found herself smiling at that fact. She read:

"*PRINCIPLE #4:* The power of a Keep-InTouch program."

Susie said, smiling again at the opened

 combination lock, "Well, I certainly get the metaphor."

Highground cocked his head toward her. "And after you meet my four 'principled' friends, you will find out it is much more than just a metaphor. Lots of things will open up for you—when you remember the combination, of course."

Susie shook her head slightly, somewhat overwhelmed, and closed the notebook. "Do I keep this then?"

"Sure do. Bring it tomorrow, along with your favorite pen, because you are going to be writing some very important notes under each principle as the hours go by."

With that, Highground got up. "Well, I bet you're tired and a little confused. But I hope you're also excited about tomorrow."

Susie stood up, too. "Yes," she said truthfully. "You know, I am. Thank you."

Highground grinned from ear to ear. "Oh, don't thank me yet. You're just starting on the journey. Be here at 8 a.m. to meet Sheila Marie. I'll meet you afterwards, okay?"

"You won't be here at 8 a.m.?" Susie suddenly felt a little overwhelmed again.

"Sheila Marie will take very good care of you. Trust me. She's Relational/Relational. You'll find out very quickly what that means. She's a fun

35

person and she really is excited about meeting you
and helping you tomorrow morning." He cocked
his head. "Know why? Because it's her nature. It's
who she is." With a wave, Highground was already
moving toward the door. "You're going to have a
great two days, Susie," he called back over his
shoulder. And then he disappeared.

Or that's at least what it seemed like to Susie.
She looked quickly around. The coffee shop was
still the soothing, fun place it always was.

But something felt different.

Susie reached down and touched her notebook.

"Isn't he a great person?" a voice said from
behind her, rushing by with a load of coffee mugs
in his hands. It was Chuck. "So is Sheila Marie. See
you in the morning."

How did Chuck know? With a slightly bemused
shake of her head, Susie waved at Chuck, picked
up the notebook, and walked outside. And as she
walked to her car, she glanced around, as if she
might see this mysterious Mr. Highground again.

Susie's eyebrows popped high at that surprising
reflex. "I guess that's a good sign," she said to
herself. But, you know, she was looking forward
to the next morning She truly was.

Chapter 3

THE NEXT MORNING, 8 A.M. SHARP, SUSIE WALKED slowly into the coffee shop and looked around. Sheila Marie Deveroux, dressed in a flattering pale blue linen dress and a bright scarf, was at the same back table, this time, though, with a different couple, a rather dignified grey-haired man and woman, both in their 70s.

Hesitantly, Susie stopped at the oak bar. "Good morning, Susie. The usual?" It was Chuck. Susie smiled hello and nodded, looking back at Sheila Marie.

"Yep. That's her," Chuck said, to Susie's surprise.

"You know about my appointment?" she asked.

"Sure," Chuck answered, handing her coffee to her and ringing up her payment. "You'll like her. But then she's Relational/Relational." Before Susie could comment on that, he was off to another customer.

Susie watched Sheila Marie quietly for a moment and realized why she looked so familiar. She recognized her face from what seemed like half the "for sale" signs around town. And suddenly Susie felt quite intimidated.

This isn't going to work, she said to herself, and actually took a step back toward the door. But then she caught Sheila Marie's eye, and instantly she was bathed in the glow of a 100 watt smile sent all the way across the cafe directly at her. Or at least she thought it was for her. Considering they'd never met, Susie glanced behind her, then to her left and then her right just to make sure, then cut her eyes slowly back toward Sheila Marie. And yes, the woman was smiling at her.

Sheila Marie waved at her, held up a finger to signal, "Just a minute," then stood up to walk the couple toward the door, so close to where Susie stood she could not help but overhear the end of their conversation.

The well-to-do couple was wanting to move to the area and start over for personal reasons. And Sheila Marie was listening. Oh, she was listening. She seemed to listen very, very well, and from the look she was giving the couple, she seemed to be genuinely moved by what she was hearing. At one point, she even touched the older woman's arm comfortingly.

"So you think that house will be able to be

fitted for our daughter and her son's special needs?" the woman asked Sheila Marie.

Sheila Marie's answer was revealing. She didn't answer with talk of the real estate market or the dollar signs of a quick sell. Instead, she said, "If it isn't, we'll find another, but we'll know as soon as my contractor friend takes a look."

The couple glanced at each other, relieved.

And then Sheila Marie added, her voice quieter: "I know I've said this before, but I want you to really believe it. Moving in to a new area and knowing no one is hard for anybody, much less when you have such a crisis going on. When my clients buy a house, I feel I also am responsible in part for their new lives, so please don't hesitate to see me as your neighborhood connection. And beyond that, if I can ever help, now or a year from now with any difficulties with your grandson, just let me know. My assistant and I do this for a living because, to be candid, we love to help."

The old man seemed very pleased. "What George said about you is true, Sheila Marie. Isn't that so, Maggie?"

The older woman sighed with what seemed to Susie like thorough relief. And Sheila Marie seemed to revel in it. "We'll meet after lunch, okay?" she told them as they said goodbye.

And then before Susie could move, Sheila Marie had turned the buoyant feeling her way and was striding toward her.

"Susie? You are Susie McCumber, right? David Highground has a talent for describing people."

"Yes, I'm Susie."

"Wonderful. Highground has told me all about you. He says you have great things in your future."

Susie couldn't help but feel a bit buoyed by those words herself even though she had her personal doubts about the matter. "Well," she said, a little embarrassed, "he keeps telling me that."

"Believe it. I've never known him to be wrong. Come on, let's take a ride. I need to look at another listing for that couple, just in case the news on the house they picked is not good."

Susie could barely put down her coffee cup before Sheila Marie had whisked her through the door to her waiting car—a white Mercedes with a personalized license plate that said: Sheila Marie.

Nestled comfortably in the tan leather upholstery of the beautiful car, Susie said what she was thinking. "You know, I admire how much in control you are of your life, Sheila Marie. You are so successful and comfortable."

"Oh, it wasn't always like this." Sheila Marie cut her eye toward Susie as she turned the corner. "When I was referred to David, I was not in control of anything. In fact, my nerves were so frayed and my self-esteem was so bad that I could hardly function. But David said, 'Sheila Marie, the problem is you are a Relational/Relational person trying to convince the world you are a Business/Business person.' All my effort wasn't working because I was putting on the wrong face. I was not putting on my face. You know?" Sheila Marie shined that bright smile Susie's way. Susie couldn't help but smile back.

"But what does Relational/Relational really mean?"

"Well, that's a good question, and I think Highground will explain it to you in full detail this afternoon. But, for me, it means that I'm the kind of person who loves people, and values relationships so highly that I will always, naturally, put them before my business and financial needs. But that always made me think that I couldn't be a good businesswoman. Trust me, I was never at risk of putting the 'program' ahead of the relationship with my clients. Business/Relational people and especially Business/Business people are always at risk of seeming like their motives are driven purely by profit. Not me. The problem was I wasn't making a living, no matter how much I loved the people I worked with. Then I met David Michael Highground. With some simple coaching, he helped me start up a system of work that fits my personality, my life—and within less than four months, my business completely changed."

They turned at the stoplight and drove into the town's nicest section of homes. "Do you real-

41

ly think, though, the same system that works for you can work for what I do? What I mean to say is, you're a realtor with big commissions on each sale, and all that. I'm not sure it can be the same for what I do."

They stopped at a stop sign, and Sheila Marie looked at Susie. "Let me answer that question with some questions you answer for yourself, okay?"

"Okay."

And Sheila Marie quoted them without pause:

"Do relationships count in your business?

"How much would one client treated well buy of your product in a lifetime?

"How would you feel about a marketing system that lets you be you, enthusiastic but not overly aggressive?

"Would you rather be known for your interest in the well-being of your customers than for the fees you can make from them?

"Would you rather wake up each morning confident that you have a system that works for you using the most powerful and most economical marketing system known to mankind—word of mouth?"

Susie smiled. "I take it these questions are rhetorical."

Sheila Marie cocked her head at her passenger. "In a way. But in a way, not at all. And I've saved the best for last. This is the one that David Highground wants me to explain to you:

"Wouldn't you want a trained sales force of 250 people you don't have to pay telling the people they know how great you and your business are?"

Susie almost laughed. "Who wouldn't?"

"Exactly," she said, pulling up to the curb of the property she wanted to eyeball. "Have you heard that one before?"

Susie pulled her new notebook from her satchel. "Mr. Highground gave me this notebook. And that sounds rather like the first principle in it. Right?"

"Yes," said Sheila Marie. **Principle #1 The 250x250 Rule.** It's not who you know, it's who your clients know that is important. Or as I like to put it, it's not only the people who you know that counts, it's also who your client knows. And for a person like me, well, it's like having 250x250 potential friends. Everyday I look forward to who I might meet." She laughed at herself. "Oh, sweetie, I do love that part of my work. In fact, I can't imagine a life without it now. It's hard to believe that just two years ago I spent more money on scheme after scheme to find new clients, everything from direct mail to advertising.

"I even had a telemarketer working for me. Can you believe that! Here I was, a person who hates cold calling, trying to motivate someone to do what I hate and hate having done to me! Talk

43

about ironic! And my broker actually asked me if I would train other realtors how to do it!" Sheila Marie shook her head. "It seems incredible now. And what's worse is I almost did it because I was SO financially successful with my telemarketing skills that I needed the money!"

Sheila Marie looked at Susie and Susie looked at Sheila Marie. And they instantly broke out laughing. It felt good.

"Oh, good grief," Sheila Marie said, wiping the laughing tears from her eyes. "It's crazy, isn't it?"

"Yes, it is," Susie said, running her hand over the nice leather interior. "I'm beginning to think maybe it's crazy like a fox, though."

"Now you're understanding."

"I do have a question though. What if you don't know 250 people?"

"I'm glad you asked that question, Ms. McCumber," Sheila Marie said in her best marketing seminar teaching voice. And then she belly-laughed again. "How many people do you think you know?"

"Well, I don't know. Maybe 100, if I really work at counting right."

"You'll be doing that soon. And you'll be very surprised to find out that you probably know quite a few more than that. I certainly was when I tried to answer that question. Highground told me I knew 250 people. He was pretty close, I have to admit. He then taught me The 250x250 Rule—that if I simply take care of the 250 people I know, and become consistent with the rest of his simple system based on relationships, I could actually motivate them, through taking an interest in them, to refer me to the 250 people they know. Are you good at math?"

Susie did a quick mental calculation. "But Sheila Marie, that's impossible. That's over 62,500!"

"Isn't that wonderful? That's the number I could think of as my client base because they should be thinking of me if they ever needed a realtor. Why? Because one of their friends is someone I've kept in contact with or done good business with. And if I have done a good job

I KNOW ED, JOE, KAREN, BOB, SUE, HARRIET, JOAN, FRANK, TONY, GARY...

45

Principle #1: The 250x250 Rule.

with the first 250, if I have proven to be trustworthy and professional, they will all enjoy referring
me. That's just basic good, human nature.
Another way to look at it for my specific business
is the average person in this town moves every five
years. If I only take care of the people I know and
gain their business when they make a move, then
I'll do 50 transactions a year. Not bad when you
consider the average realtor in this country does
less than 15 a year."

"Okay, but Sheila Marie, I really don't know
250 people."

"Oh yes, you do."

"Oh, no I don't."

Sheila Marie giggled. "Oh, yes, sweetie, you do.
That's exactly what I said, and you know what? I
did know 250 people. I may not have kept up with
them the way I should have, but I knew 'em. And
when I got through learning and enacting Principle
#4, they heard from me. And everything began
to happen."

Susie shook her head. "You've really got it figured out."

"Now I do, perhaps. I certainly didn't before I
met Highground."

"But Sheila Marie, I still say it sounds too good,
too simple. Why doesn't everybody rely on that
good basic human nature you mentioned, and we
all live on referrals and relationships?"

Sheila Marie opened her car door. "Come on in

with me and we'll keep talking."

As Sheila Marie herded Susie inside the empty
house and began to put her studied eye to the
place, she asked Susie: "I have a good analogy.
Do you work out?"

"Yes."

"Do you find it simple? Easy to keep doing?"

Susie looked at Sheila Marie rather non-
plussed. "Well, not exactly. If I didn't meet my
friend for Jazzercise three times a week, I'm sure
I wouldn't. But I keep up."

"You have a simple routine and you're confident it will keep you healthy and trim, right?"

"Right."

"Then if it's that simple, why do the majority
of the people in this country have a problem
with weight?"

"You're saying it's because they don't follow
a routine system?"

"Or they start one and then, as you say, fall
off the wagon."

"I knew there was a catch," Susie said with a
sigh, leaning against a door frame as Sheila Marie
inspected here, there, and everywhere.

"But such a nice one," Sheila Marie added.

Having seen enough, Sheila Marie made shoo-
ing motions toward the front door which tickled
Susie. She liked this woman. It was hard not to.

Once outside, Sheila Marie put her hands on
her hips and stopped to enjoy the warm sunshine

47

for a second. "Beautiful day, isn't it?"

Susie glanced around. Yes, it was. She hadn't really noticed.

And when she looked back toward Sheila Marie, Sheila Marie had already put herself back into high gear toward the car. Susie had to hustle to catch up. As Sheila Marie unlocked the car, she smiled across the car's roof at Susie and said, "Did Highground ask you the three questions?"

"Let's see: 'Do I like myself?' 'Do I believe in my product?' And 'Can I stay the course?' Those three?"

"Those three. And the last one is the deal-buster, but it's like your exercise program. You probably enjoy it now, don't you? You'd miss it if you didn't have it."

"That's right."

"Then you'll do fine. We all get busy. And we think we don't have time to stop and put into practice some foundational truths that we really want to live by. All it takes is understanding yourself and then understanding the lifetime value of a relationship over a commission check. Instead of wandering around with dollar signs in your eyes as I did— oh, I was a mess—you stride ahead with a willingness to help people get what they need. And that's so much more fun, not to mention fulfilling."

As they cruised back toward the coffee shop, Sheila Marie said, "So what do you think, Ms. Susie McCumber? Do you understand Principle #1

48

enough that I can send you on to Principle #2?"

"I think."

Sheila Marie touched Susie's arm. "See here, sweetie. You just trust the simple system that Highground is going to show you today and tomorrow, and then shift that thinking of yours just a little and I am here to tell you that it will change your life. It did for me. Let me have your card. I'm going to keep up with you, see how you're doing, okay?"

They pulled up to the cafe. Susie opened the door, got out, and then handed one of her business cards back to Sheila Marie. Sheila Marie Deveroux handed Susie one of her business cards in return. Then, she said, just before she put the car into gear: "Keep that card now, and just let me know if there is anything else I can do for you, including house hunting. Remember! It's not only the people you know that count, but who your clients know as well! I'll be talking to you!"

And with an affectionate wave, Sheila Marie drove away.

"Susie!"

Susie turned around to find Mr. David Michael Highground coming her way, and there was a man with him, the man he had pointed out the day before in the cafe.

"So, Susie, how was your morning?" Highground said.

"Great," was her honest answer. "Sheila Marie

49

is quite an interesting woman."

Highground laughed. "That she is. Did she give you a good understanding of Principle #1?"

"The 250 x250 Rule. 'It's not only who you know but also who your clients know.' Right?"

"That's it. I want you to meet Paul Kingston, Susie. Paul, this is the young lady I was telling you about. Susan McCumber. Her friends call her Susie."

Paul was a rather short, average-looking man with thinning sandy hair, pleasant enough, but nothing that you'd remember upon first meeting him. He was the kind of man who gets underestimated. And that's what Susie did.

"Hello," she said.

"It's a pleasure to meet you," Paul said, clasping Susie's outstretched hand with both of his. Susie found herself looking at him again.

"Paul wants us to have lunch with him. Can you do it?"

"Yes. Certainly," replied Susie.

"Okay, then. We've still got about 30 minutes before our reservation, so it's a good time for your first assignment. And Paul and I have some things to catch up on. So. Got that pen or pencil I suggested you bring today?"

She patted her satchel. "Yes, I do."

"And your notebook."

"And my notebook."

Highground handed her a tape and a headset. "I've made this just for you. Mostly it's my favorite classical music. Go sit over at the harbor, listen to it, do as it says, and we'll be back to get you by noon. We'll have lunch at the Capri restaurant right over there." He pointed a few blocks down the oceanfront. "Okay?"

As soon as she took the tape and headset from his hand, they were gone. She looked out on the harbor, then back at her handful, and roamed over to the bench that overlooked the cliffs, the sailboats and the beautiful California coastline that she loved so much.

To her surprise, she realized how long it had been since she allowed herself to relax long enough to enjoy the view. Breathing in the salt air and listening to the gulls, she pulled out her notebook, her pencil, and then put the tape in the player and the headset on her head. And this is what she heard to a soundtrack of Mozart:

"Susie. For the next few minutes, I want you to take the first step toward making this system work for you. In the space provided after Principle #1 in your Highground notebook, you'll note several pages are numbered from 1 to 250.

"As an exercise to make you see and believe how many relationships, old and new, you have, I want you to list all the people you know—through school years, church, family, and your daily interactions such as the grocer and the dry cleaners. Acquaintances count when you see them all the time, such as the convenience store

51

clerk or your mechanic. My educated guess is
you'll be able to list 100 people fairly confidently,
and the rest you may have to be coached to recov-
er from neglect or forgetfulness. So, enjoy my
music and get to work!"

Susie stared at the notebook's pages and all
those numbers for a frozen second, then she started racing to put down the story of her relational
life: Her sisters, her pastor, her friends at her old
job. Her teachers. Her doctor and her dentist and
her insurance salesman. Chuck down at the coffee
shop, Jane, the hairdresser, Amy, the shampoo girl.
Joni, her favorite waitress at her favorite lunch spot.

She was on a roll.

My goodness, she thought. Look at all these
people I know. And she began to write faster—
she couldn't wait to see how many she could
name before Highground returned.

Chapter 4

B Y THE TIME SHE FELT A TAP ON HER SHOULDER, she had listed over 150 people. She couldn't believe it.

Highground must have read her mind again. "Told you so," he said.

She took off the headset and stood up. "Incredible."

"You'll have your 250 easy with a little more work," Highground assured her.

"Ready for lunch?" Paul asked.

"Famished."

As they walked toward the restaurant, Susie asked, "What do you do, Paul?"

Paul glanced at Highground with a grin and answered, "I'm in the business of being comfortable with who I am so I can help others achieve their goals—to get where they want to go. Our Mr. Highground here says that I'm Relational/ Business. I'm with a tremendous company that produces a variety of quality products, and it's through this company that I have helped hundreds become financially independent and enjoy their lives."

"Paul's in network marketing," Highground added.

"I certainly am."

Susie was taken back by the whole exchange. Suddenly this man did not seem so short or average-looking. The confidence of this man almost unnerved her. She could only wish for such confidence in the sales talk she had studied, and she heard herself blurt out, "Where does your confidence come from? It's infectious."

Paul laughed, affectionately clamping a hand on Highground's shoulder. "When I was at my own crossroads, or as Highground likes to say, 'on the mantel,' this man came to me through a friend and spent time helping me as no one else ever had. He was the first to tell me that I didn't have to imitate anyone else, that the gifts I had been given at birth were more than enough for those around me if only I would allow them to be, and be consistent in doing so.

"I spent a couple of days just like you are doing, with Highground's ideas, and it opened my eyes to a better and more simple way of doing things. I learned firsthand how not to put my products and my money-making opportunities before my relationships with others, because when

I did, people were seeing right through me. And I learned how to stand in front of a group of people and enjoy being me, a short, plain-looking relational/business type of guy who is extremely successful doing it."

"Yes," Highground added with a grin, "you certainly are."

"And proud of it. This all happened for me, Susie, when I followed our Mr. Highground's little system and trusted it to produce all the results I need. I am 'doing business from the high ground,'" Paul added, with a nod toward David Highground as they walked. "That's a little phrase a few of us coined in honor of your work with us, David. The high ground is where we all want to be strategically in business, but more importantly, it's synonymous with the 'high road,' you know? Always trying to do the right thing."

"Thank you, Paul. I appreciate that."

They had arrived at the restaurant door, and Paul gallantly opened it and held it open for them.

When they were finally seated, with a view of the harbor and the bluff, they could see, on the horizon, a freighter steaming out to sea.

Susie watched a few seconds, then she looked across at the mysterious David Highground and finally asked what she'd been wanting to ask all day. "Mr. Highground, I asked Sheila Marie about being called

Relational/Relational' and she said you would
explain it all in detail. Would you? I'd like to know
what I am."

Nodding, Highground turned his gaze to the
freighter for a moment, then said: "I've been helping folks for as long as I can remember, Susie, and
I finally concluded that it is wrong to try to change
people into something they are not. Since God
provided all of us with our unique individual gifts,
what I should do is meet people where they are
and help them be more of what they are.
Someone said that we are all three types of
individuals—first, the one that we think we are,
second, the one others think we are, and third,
the one we truly are. By taking the time to look
at ourselves and asking others whom we trust, we
can identify who we think we are and how others
see us. And by doing that, we can actually get very
close to who we really are."

Paul looked up momentarily from this menu.
"And we can stop wondering what the 'personality
du jour" has to be. Hmmm. Look at the soup du
jour—Boston clam chowder. I think I'll have that."

"Susie," Highground went on, "do you remember the four windows of business personalities I
rushed through with you yesterday?"

"Yes and no."

Highground grabbed four paper napkins, pulled
a pen from his pocket and began to scribble. The
first words were:

RELATIONAL/RELATIONAL

"The four types are split into two words," he explained, pushing the napkin toward Susie. "The word on the left of the slash mark represents how people see you and who you are naturally. The word on the right of the slash mark is your natural tendency in business relationships. The Relational/Relational person is one others see as someone who only thinks of relationships with others, how to help and how to be liked or even loved. They rarely think of the business ramifications, or if they do, will justify them immediately in some relational way. So the second word has to be relational, too."

He then scribbled:

RELATIONAL/BUSINESS

He pushed that napkin toward Susie, too. "The second is a person who is very relational when meeting people and is truly interested in the relationship first, but when the talk turns to business, the person will begin to think strategically."

On the third napkin, he wrote:

BUSINESS/RELATIONAL

"Note which comes first here." He placed the napkin on top of the other two in front of Susie. "The third one is the reverse of that. It's a person who doesn't come off at first glance as interested in a relationship as much as pure business, but will develop deep relationships after the business is established."

He took the last napkin and wrote across it:
BUSINESS/BUSINESS

"And the final trait is Business/Business, which is simply the opposite of Relational/Relational. This person usually has a hard time with our little system based on relationships until he or she justifies the time spent with those they've affected in some sort of pure business way. Which they always do." He placed this final napkin on top of the rest.

"So, is one better than the other?" Susie asked, rather earnestly.

"Absolutely not. There is no right, no wrong. There is simply who we are and why we need to be comfortable

with ourselves. But," he went on, "it's important to note that without consistency and a plan, all traits are equally ineffective."

"Note that," Paul suggested.

So Highground took out another napkin and wrote the idea across it and placed it on top of all the rest.

Paul went on. "My biggest hurdle was that I was a relational guy. I met lots of people and I did not always invest my time with the right people—until I took the high ground and started using this system to build a database, ABC it, and strategically lay out a plan the right way first, so I wouldn't have to do it ever again."

"ABC...it?"

"That's right. And that's next. Now, let's eat!" Paul demanded.

❖   ❖   ❖   ❖

The three finished lunch and ordered coffee.

"The main thing I want you to know," Paul explained to Susie, "is because you were referred to me by Highground, I am at your disposal."

"And now I'm going to leave you two to chat," Highground said, getting up. "I'll be back."

"When?" Susie asked, wishing he wouldn't keep disappearing.

"Oh, I'll know when to come back," he said, as mysterious as always. And he was gone.

"A great guy, eh?" Paul said. "Well, he asked me to explain Principle #2, and so I shall. I'm going to show you how to do business only with the people you want to and on your terms! Sound good?"

Susie smiled. This man was warm, but he was also very business-like when it came to specifics.

She liked that. "So, you're relational/business. I wonder if that's what I am," Susie said.

The coffee came and Paul took a sip. "Well, for me, the funny thing about being relational/business is although I have business tacked on to my trait, I did not always execute in a businesslike manner. It's not that I didn't know how, I just didn't have a system in place."

"Oh, but you seem very business-like to me."

Paul gave her a nod. "Well, thank you. But I had to work at keeping it focused, let me tell you. Ready to hear all about Principle #2?"

"Let's see." She flipped through the notebook. "Here it is. Build a database and ABC it. You're going to tell me what it means?"

"Sure am. What I'm going to show you is how to rate and communicate with your entire database and what happens when you do! Got your note-book? Turn to your 250x250 list."

She obeyed. And pushed it toward him.

Paul looked it over. "Looks good. Now, Sheila Marie helped you understand the power of your database—that's what this list is, a database. What I want to share with you is how to make it work properly. You have to ABC it just as Highground taught me to do."

"ABC it," Susie echoed.

"That's right. ABC it. Highground also convinced me that I needed a full time assistant to help me follow up. That was a very big commit-

Principle #2: Build a database and ABC it.

ment starting out. But when you get to Principle #4, you'll see how that might sound feasible to you, too. Even if it sounds crazy right now."

Susie frowned.

"Okay, let me see if I can put it into an image." Paul thought a minute. "Do you have certain people that are absolutely your cheerleaders, ones that would stand up and speak a good word about you right now, ones that feel so strongly about you and your products that they would refer you right now?"

Susie perked up. "Sure, I'm thinking of several right now, several who already have."

"Fantastic," Paul exclaimed, smile beaming. "Those are your A's, your power base. Your A's are the ones that are most likely to refer you.

61

They are your advocates, your champions. Now, who are your B's?"

"That's my line," Susie said.

"Oh, right. Excuse me." Paul laughed. "Okay, well, your B's are individuals that you think can champion your cause as well as refer you if you educate them how you work and if you keep in good, consistent contact with them. Your whole focus with B's are to move them to A's."

"And the C's?"

"The C category are the ones you are not sure about, but want to keep communicating with. You are not sure that even with the proper communication and education they would champion your cause as well as refer you, but you hope that they would," he said.

Paul was now on a roll. "Now, the last category is almost as important as the first. This is the one that actually gives you the ability to control your business to some extent. That is the D category. The D category is synonymous with delete. The individuals you are certain are ones that you do not want to work with."

"You're kidding. I get to choose?"

Paul smiled wryly. "There's an old saying that we are judged not only by the people that we do business with but also by the people we choose not to do business with. So, yes. It's a no-thank-you list. An I'd-rather-not-do-business-with-you list."

"Wow."

"Nice thought, isn't it? To be able to say no?"

"Nice? It sounds impossible," Susie marveled. "But how do you set this all up? What do you say? How often do you say it, and what do they say in response?"

"Slow down," Paul laughed again. "We'll get to all those good questions in due time. This is a step by step process. Besides, Highground has already figured out all of that and made it easy to implement."

"Really?"

"Hey. Really. It's why we are sitting here. He's saving the best until last." Paul opened up his briefcase. "Now. I've got something to show you. I brought along a printed copy of my database separated by A's, B's and C's." He pulled a stapled, computer print-out from his briefcase and handed it to Susie.

Susie studied it a moment and said, "Wow, Paul. You certainly have fewer A's than I would have expected."

"That's by choice, Susie. The most precious commodity we all have is time. I communicate in writing, and, in many cases, personally each month with my A's. I am very careful who becomes one of my A's. They must have demonstrated the ability to champion my cause as well as refer me and be a power advocate for me. These are the people I spend most of my time and marketing dollars on. I believe Highground

has you set up to visit Sara Simpson tomorrow.
She will show you what I mean in that arena."

"Okay."

Paul set down his briefcase. "Before I had this
system, I was letting business happen to me instead
of doing business in a proactive way. Now, I
actually train all the new people I work with in this
system. I get a real kick out of helping people get
over the biggest hurdle in business—finding new
qualified individuals to do business with regularly.
And I'm not talking about 'spray and pray marketing' anymore."

Susie shook her head. "Thank goodness. I
detest that."

"Me, too. What I'm referring to is having the
opportunity to meet people on the strong recom-
mendation of their friends and associates and to do
so regularly. Just like you were referred here to me
by Highground. He spoke highly of me, didn't he?"

"Sure did," Susie confirmed.

"By the time I walked up to meet you I was
already delivered to you on a pedestal, wasn't I?"
Paul asked.

"Well, yes. He couldn't say enough nice things."

"And that's a nice pedestal to be on, even if I
have to make very sure I don't tumble off it by
continuing to do my work in an excellent way.
That's what the system is all about. When we really
think about our past, haven't all the significant
relationships, business or personal for the most

part, come out of a referral? A middle person building you up without you having to do that yourself?"

"Absolutely," she again confirmed. "It's not what you say about yourself that people believe anyway, it's what others say about you that they believe."

That made Paul belly laugh. "My goodness, Susie, you sound like Highground! You're getting it! So doesn't it make sense to have a system in place that will allow you to do that everyday? That is what ABC-ing your database will do for you. It will give you the ability to be proactive with all the people you know now and all that you will meet in the future. Now you will look at each of your friends and business acquaintances as a lifelong relationship. You will no longer feel rushed to push your business with everyone you meet immediately other than the ones that it make sense to."

"So, did Paul teach you your ABCs?"

It was Highground. He was back, standing by their table.

Paul looked at his watch. "It's 3:00 o'clock, already? Where has the time gone? Susie, I have a little meeting in 15 minutes. We thought you might enjoy being there. I'm training some new people that have joined my organization—giving them an overview of the system. Want to join me?"

65

"Sounds great," Susie said.

"We thought you'd say that," Highground said. "Shall we go?"

For the next hour, Susie sat next to Highground, mesmerized by the confident Paul as he talked about his products, about their opportunity and about the lifelong value of relationships instead of commissions to seven new distributors of his company.

Now Susie was getting excited. She could taste it. That was her in front of those seven, as soon as she could get the system up and operational.

After the session, Susie asked for Paul's card and put a big A on the back so he could see it. Then she smiled, shook his hand and thanked him for a very revealing afternoon.

Highground and Susie walked down the street towards the coffee shop where her adventure had begun.

Susie had a million questions. "Paul said you had everything planned out, when to do what, how to do what, and all that? Is that true?"

"Well, yes it is." Highground smiled. He always enjoyed watching the light go on with his protegés. Susie looked and acted completely different from the morning before. She was starting to get the vision.

"All large companies have a marketing plan for at least a year in advance. They brand themselves with a certain image and every employee has to align themselves with it, yet continue to figure out all by themselves how to find their customers. What I do for folks like you is give you a powerful marketing plan with a personalized brand based on truth that allows you to not have to think about it after you initiate it. And if that is even too overwhelming at first, or if you just don't want to do it yourself, I can get you outside help to implement it. But that's jumping ahead to Principle #4."

Susie pulled her notebook from her satchel and flipped to the right page, and read:

"Let's see: PRINCIPLE #4: The power of an 'In Touch' program."

Highground grinned from ear to ear. "That's right. But before we can get there, we have to learn what to say when we do try to stay in touch, don't we? That's the next principle."

Susie flipped back a few pages, and read to herself: PRINCIPLE #3 Just Let Me Know— Educate your clients through what you say and what you send them on a consistent basis.

She looked up at Highground and sighed.

Highground cocked his head toward her, understanding everything she was feeling. "Susie, what I would like you to do is go to a quiet place tonight and think about the day. I have given you a little outline for some goals. You'll find it in your notebook. Continue the exercise tonight and journal your plans. And I'll

see you at 8:00 sharp tomorrow morning. Philip
and Sara will be teaching you the next two very
important principles. And don't worry. They do a
super job of teaching them."

"I want you to know how much I appreciate
your help," Susie said.

"The pleasure is all mine," Highground said
with a smile. "See you in the morning."

Susie started to walk away and turned to mention one more thing, but Highground was gone.
Again. She smiled and shook her head. Who is this
guy anyway?

What a day, she thought, what-a-day!

❖   ❖   ❖   ❖

At home that night, she sat down and opened
her notebook and found her assignment in a
section marked GOALS. Attached was a little note
from Highground:

Dear Susie,
By now, you have found out that you know a
lot more people than you thought you knew, and
you've begun to grasp the power of The 250x250
Rule of Principle #1. You also know that having a
list is not enough. You know Principle #2, that the
list has to be ABC'ed to make it work for you. You
know now how much nicer and easier it is to be
"pulled" in by your clients instead of "pushing"

your way in.

So before we go on, here's your assignment. I'm a big believer in the power of goals to make things happen. One of my favorite sayings is, "If you don't know where you are going, any road will take you there." And another great favorite of mine is, "Success is a Goal with a Deadline." So we are going to create some goals, short ones. Long range ones are great for seeing the big picture, but short range ones get things going.

On the next two pages are two sheets already designed to get you going. Changing your perspective is helped by imagining yourself already putting these principles into action in your life.

Postdate Goal #1 for two weeks from today. Postdate Goal #2 for 8 weeks from today. And then put on your best imagining cap and project yourself and where you'd LIKE to be on both those dates. Don't be bashful. You have what it takes.

Good luck!

Best,

D. M. Highground

Susie turned the page and there was a page with sentences and blanks all set up. So Susie began to write. And this is what her two goals pages looked like after she was finished:

GOAL #1

Goal: *Finish my 250x250 list and then orga-nize them. Put the first action to my new mindset.*

Goal Date: *2 weeks from today*

The date is *July 1* **and I have:** *Spent the last 2 weeks laying out my goal and spending much needed time in planning out my new marketing plan for my business. I now have fully realized the importance of a relationship over my short-term financial gain, and I know that it is good business to spend more time developing my relationship for their lifetime value. I have taken to heart that I truly can communicate with thousands of people on a personal level through the 250 on my list.*

I have already experienced: *a complete rever-sal of the boxed-in mindset I had at the coffee shop two weeks ago. I look forward to my day.*

I feel: *that I have a handle on where I am going because I now have a proven plan on how I operate each day.*

I am excited about: *Having this system fully operational on a daily basis and seeing regular results from it.*

My associates and colleagues are: *impressed with my new direction. They are asking questions about my new approach. They are seeing a confidence in me that is attributable to being myself rather than trying to imitate others.*

I am determined to: *each day make progress*

*in reaching the other goals I have taken the time
to write out and review regularly.*

GOAL #2

Goal: *Having my 250x250 database ABC'd
and in use*
Goal Date: *8 weeks from today*
The date is *Aug. 1* **and I have:** *just reviewed
my database of over 250 names. I have all four
categories listed ABC and the D's and can access
them by each category with a push of the button.
I can mail merge a letter in seconds. I now know
through experiential knowledge that this is the
only marketing plan I will ever need. I have
already started to communicate with them
through an initial mailing outlining their
importance to me.*
  I have already experienced: *15 solid
referrals in the process of setting up and communicating with my database of 250 people. Calling
these referrals has been so enjoyable because I
have been asked to do so. As Highground said, I
have been pulled in instead of pushing in.*

  I feel: *more in control of my day and more
positive because I actually have a proven proactive
daily plan for my business and have experienced
results. I feel good about myself as if I have found
a place I fit in the business world by being myself.*
  I am excited about: *learning and imple-*

menting the "Keep-InTouch" program that will make all that I learned into a true system for my life.

My associates and colleagues are: *viewing me as a competent business person because of the discipline I have developed in my business. Several have asked me to share my secret.*

I am determined to: *stay the course and become extremely competent in this process and further develop my style and personal skills around it.*

Susie set down her pencil and smiled. It actually worked. She imagined herself in the future. And she liked what she imagined.

She put down the notebook, turned out the light and fell asleep looking forward, for the first time in a long time, to the day ahead.

Chapter 5

SHE AWOKE EARLIER THAN USUAL THE NEXT MORN-
ING. The sun had not quite risen over the
mountains to the east of Rancho Benecia.
But she couldn't go back to sleep. In fact, she
couldn't wait to get up. Her mind was racing,
and, for the first time in weeks, in a positive, not
a negative way. And it felt good, so very good.
All the ideas and hopes and shared stories of the
last two days had taken hold of her in a powerful, uplifting way that surprised her. She not only
was experiencing a perception change of her
situation, but after last night's goal-setting, she
was also developing a plan of action that was
real and not contrived like some of the plans
she'd been taught.

In the past, when she heard something she didn't much like while attending a training, she would gloss over those parts like cold calling or handling objections and asking closing questions. She wasn't doing it this time. And that's because she saw none of those things (especially cold calling—oh how she hated cold calling) in this play. None at all.

So she showered, put on one of her best outfits, because she wanted to look as good as she felt this morning, and within minutes, she was strolling down Main Street overlooking the ocean. The morning fog had not burned off yet. There was a newness to this time of the day that she liked. And this morning it felt newer still, newer than ever before. And she knew why. She checked her satchel again to make sure she had her notebook, because she was actually looking forward to reviewing the goals she had written last night with Highground.

By the time she got to the coffee shop, Highground was already there looking over the display case of tempting pastries.

"Good morning, Susie!" he chimed, as buoyant as she felt herself. "Ready to start?"

"I've never been more ready in my life," she stated.

"Great. Let's get one of these pastries, order up our coffee, grab a table to review your thoughts from yesterday, and then I'll tell you what you'll experience today."

Within a few minutes, the two were seated at a front table, coffee cups and pastries and notebooks strewn between them. And as Highground looked over Susie's filled-in goals, his smile grew bigger and bigger and bigger.

"What?" Susie had to know.

"I just love seeing someone like you getting 'it'."

Susie picked up her cup and leaned back confidently in her chair. "You mean, understanding the lifetime value of a relationship—the value of what that person might purchase in a lifetime as well as the value of their lifetime referrals with the right communication through a properly organized database that's been ABC'ed and written as an 8-week goal?"

Highground laid back his head and laughed loud and hardy. "You're doing fabulous, Susie. You're already applying the system to your own style. I'm truly looking forward to seeing the bright future peeking out from your first two goals in the next 8 weeks."

"I appreciate that, Mr. Highground," said Susie, "but I have to admit something. I may be a little uncomfortable telling people that I work this way when I don't—yet. That's the next step, isn't it? I have to start from scratch?"

Highground nodded. "Great observation. Everyone I help through this process has the same hurdle. What you will learn this morning with Philip is how first to educate yourself, then educate any staff or people that will work with you, then finally educate your clients on your database—your 250x250 list that's been ABC'ed. But first, as I said, you have to teach yourself. You have to live the system in order to have the confidence to share it with others. That's what being genuine is all about."

"That's a relief. The last thing I want to do is be something that I'm not," she said. "Been there, done that. Doesn't work."

"Do you know how many people never learn that? You're already half way there."

Highground pushed away from the table, seeing Philip come in the door. "Remember, Susie, Philip is a Business/Relational, so his style will be quite different from Sheila Marie's or Paul's."

Philip walked in at the appointed time, impeccably dressed as usual. "Good morning, I'm Philip Stackhouse," he said to Susie with a warm confident smile as he approached the table.

"Philip," Highground said, "this is the friend I was talking about, Susie McCumber."

"Hello, Philip," Susie answered, "it's my pleasure to meet you."

Highground waved him to pull up another chair. "Philip, I was just mentioning to Susie what you will be sharing with her this morning in regards to educating everyone on the system."

"More like indoctrination," Philip laughed, sitting down.

"Before you do, why don't you share with Susie your background and where you were before we met. I thought I would leave you two to talk for a couple of hours before your clients arrive. You are meeting them here, Philip?"

"Yes, I am."

"Well, then, I'll be back about 11:00 a.m., okay?"

"No problem," Philip said, and Susie agreed by nodding and waving to Highground as he did his disappearing act once more.

"So, Susie," Philip began, leaning toward her. "What do you think of all that you have heard and seen in the last day or so?" Philip had focused suddenly and directly at Susie, almost as if he were interrogating her.

A bit taken back by this scrutiny, Susie reverted a little into her old nervousness. The fact that Philip was obviously a highly successful individual by the way he dressed and acted didn't help. However, leaning on what she learned yesterday and the fact that she was referred by Highground with nothing to prove to this man, she looked directly at Philip and said, "I still have some questions, but what I like most is I don't have to try to impress you. I just need to be myself. That's what I saw in Sheila Marie and Paul yesterday. Also, the system seemed at first to be a bit simplistic, but I think that's only my first impression. Actually, it's beginning to sound more professional and consistent—if I follow it properly—than any plan I've ever tried, and I don't think that's just wishful thinking."

Susie had forgotten her earlier uneasiness and was on quite a roll, one that Philip noticed.

He smiled, impressed. "I think you're going to institute this system as well as anyone I know and I look forward to watching that happen. You are going to truly enjoy the results. So. Now that you understand and know the value of a relationship, have learned how to create a database and to ABC it, I'm supposed to talk to you about what you do next."

"And what's that?"

"Live it," Philip said, with a wry look. "What do you think of that?"

"Makes sense. So how did you achieve that?" Susie asked.

"One step at a time," Philip said. "Understanding how to live this system and educate others doesn't happen overnight. It begins with a perception change—first of yourself, then of others' perception of you. And when that happens, all the future people you meet will acquire the new perception immediately."

He waved to get Chuck's attention.

"The usual?" Chuck called over.

Philip shot him his trademark thumbs-up, and

went back to his conversation. "You know," he said, "I hadn't thought of it, but that's what Highground is. He's a perception-changer. The first thing he does is change our perceptions of ourselves, which in turn helps us change the perception of those around us."

"He has definitely done that for me in the last two days," Susie agreed.

"I wasn't always doing business through my database and by referral," Philip confided. "Before I met Highground I trained the financial planners in my office how to find business cold. I advertised in newspapers, on television, wherever I could spend money in the hope of making the telephone ring. I was pretty good at it. As I moved up the ladder, I always had a knack for selling. I did the 10 hours a day on the phones as a young securities salesman. I didn't get much fulfillment out of it, but thought that was how everyone did business."

"You were good at cold calls?"

"I was," Philip admitted. "I just didn't like it. Then I started my own operation and tried to train new sales people in the art of selling those old ways, and my results plummeted. What I found was there are very few of us out there who learned the techniques to handle objections, 'close hard three times,' etc. etc. etc., to the point of making them work. Rare is the person who is truly good at it or can keep it up over a long

79

time. The more my overall closing percentages
went down—because I included my staff in the
averages—the more I threw money at places to
find more leads. By the time I met Highground I
was at my wit's end. He would say I was on the
mantel. I was certainly at a crossroads in my career,
very frustrated and disheartened. I was ready to go
back to the drawing board and work the phones
for 10 hours a day. I didn't want to do that, but I
knew I could at least pay the bills."

"I know the feeling," Susie said.

"But with a little journey like you are now on, I
redirected my business and life. I'm now respected,
doing business with who I want to and have more
time to do the things I want to do. My whole staff
is trained in this system and they like themselves
and the company a lot more for it. When we use
the little term, 'Just Let Me Know,' we understand it
is a two-way street. That's why we're so confident
when we use it, because we live it."

Susie look at him, puzzled. "Just Let Me Know?"

"Oh yes. That's the linchpin in Principle #3, Just
Let Me Know—Educating your clients through what
you say and what you send them on a consistent
basis. It's what we in the High Ground Principles
of Business say to every client we work with. We
want them to let us know if we can help them in
any way in business or beyond. You'll hear specifi-
cally how to make it work with Principle #4. But
for now, just know that it's amazing in its power to

***Principle #3: Just Let Me Know—Educating your
clients through what you say and what you send them
on a consistent basis.***

give the right impression to your clients. The
last thing you want to seem is self-serving. And in
a referral system that is the most important
dynamic."

Susie was beaming at this new idea. "I like it.
It sounds genuine."

"That's because it is. That's the beauty of this
program. It's real. We help people all the time;
we go out of our way to serve our clients in ways
that the usual business philosophy would not
approve of—nor would I have, only a few years
ago. But now it's all part of our service to our
clients. When we live that out, the second part of
that phrase becomes second nature."

"What second part? You mean the referral?"

"That's right." To show her, Philip suddenly

took on his most business-like yet warm gaze, sat up professionally-straight, and said, looking straight into her eyes: "'So, Ms. Very Important Client, just let me know if we can help you in any way, business or beyond. And if you have any friends or associates that can use our services, please call me with their names. I'll treat them just as I have treated you. Just let us know.' See?"

Susie grinned. "Yes, I see. That second part is the pivotal part."

Philip nodded. "But it is give and take, and people respond to that approach. They really do. And so will you."

Susie just had a thought that made her uneasy. "Do you pay referral fees if someone sends you a client?"

Philip smiled at that. "Good question. One thing I learned from Highground is we may pay a finder's fee to someone in business if that is standard, but we never pay a referral fee. You would never expect to be paid to refer a friend to a good movie or restaurant you recommend. You do it because you have received great service or enjoyed the movie and you think your friend could benefit from knowing about it. You might be appreciated if you go to the restaurant and the owner recognizes you because you are an advocate, and that might get you faster service," he added loud enough to be heard by Chuck, who was coming their way, "much like Chuck

82

here at the coffee shop!"

"Hey, you talking about me?" Chuck said, in a joking tough voice, bringing him his coffee in a steaming mug.

"Hey, it's about time," Philip countered in an even tougher voice. "Here, take the money and leave us alone!"

Chuck laughed, grabbed the money and then shot him his trademark thumbs-up to Philip's laughing delight.

"Man, that guy is a good man. He's the reason I met Highground. And he's a walking billboard for the success of Highground's system, isn't he?"

"Chuck is involved with this system?" Susie's eyes widened at the surprise.

"Sure," Philip said, stirring his coffee and then taking a sip. "Look around at the attention to detail, the walking, talking database he has built."

"He does have a lot of friends and repeat business. You're right."

"And think about the cafe's 'items of value' you have received in the mail—coupons, discounts for other services, that sort of thing."

Susie couldn't believe she hadn't seen it before. "You're exactly right, Philip. I just realized everything—the language he uses is exactly like the language all of you are teaching me to use: How he's always asking me if he can help me in any way. And to pass his name along to any friends or family that would enjoy a good coffee

83

cafe. He even referred Mr. Highground to me! I just thought...well, I don't know what I thought. It was so natural. And helpful. Like he cared. And this cafe is so wonderfully run and its ambiance is so good, why wouldn't I tell my friends about it?"

"That's how it works, Susie. We just pass along the 'good' to those that we like and want to do business with. All of us, Chuck, Paul, Sheila Marie, and many more—we have a whole network of businesses that we are happy to refer to our clients and friends because we know that they are going to take care of them. See how it works?"

"I'm beginning to see the whole, interesting picture," Susie said.

"Which gets us back to what I'm supposed to talk to you about today—education. Now that you have changed your perception, you need to take the next step and institute some of the 'branding' of the system on your business communications, concepts like 'Just Let Me Know,' along with a host of other pieces that describe your new philosophy: Thank you cards, fax communications, pins. It needs to be part of what you say to everyone, and you have to demonstrate it daily in your business."

Susie stared at Philip's suit jacket, at something she had been noticing ever since he sat down. "What's the 'High Ground' pin all about on your lapel?" she asked. "I've been wanting to ask that since I met you. And I have a feeling that's the point."

"Susie, you are 'getting it' so well!" Philip smiled, tapping his colorful lapel pin. "Do you like it? Several years ago a few of the people who David Michael Highground had helped over the years got together and finally named his wonderful system. We call it 'The High Ground Principles of Business.' Highground said it wasn't necessary, but we wanted to do something to honor the man. He is so giving. He really doesn't ask for anything, if you'll notice. He hasn't asked anything of you, has he?"

"No, he hasn't," Susie realized.

"Well, I had to give something back to him. But it also helps me, and all of us who live our business and personal lives around this wonderful system. I've incorporated a logo around this name and then I include it unobtrusively in certain parts of my literature, explaining the value I put on a lifetime relationship. Everyone is different, so what you use to get this point across is up to you. Okay, you'd better open that notebook of yours. I'm about to give you some great information on Principle #3."

She whipped it and her pencil out, flipped quickly to the right page, and waited. "I'm ready."

"Okay. Now. Principle # 3 is—"

Susie interrupted to quote the principle to him: "Just Let Me Know—Educate your clients through what you say and what you send them consistently."

"Exactly," Philip said, and then he began in a very staccato, no-nonsense way to get down to business: "In a nutshell, it is simply the ability to communicate with everyone you know about how your business works, what you will do for them and what you expect of them in return. With your ABC'd database in order, ready and waiting, you're already halfway there. The next step is to educate yourself. When you've changed your perception of yourself and have truly begun to incorporate the language that Highground teaches you into your everyday life, you can move forward."

Susie wrote furiously, brow furrowed, fully focused, as Philip concentrated on the next point. "Next, if you will have staff working with you, then you have to get them on board. They need to have regular training and live it as well. Once those who will be working with you are on board and are living it, you are now ready to start educating your database list."

Susie looked up. "My 250x250 List? That I've ABC'd?"

"That's the one. That's your database list. And you don't have to wait until everything is in place before you start. You just have to start one step at a time.

"The first thing you will send to your ABC database is a letter telling everyone of your new business philosophy. This letter simply states the value you place on those you know and or have served in the past and the new attention you are giving to them."

"What about new people I might meet?"

"Well, it still works. Explaining this relationship system and sending them the letter as well, these people will not feel like they have an L for 'lead' on their forehead because you will not be rushing them so hard (except for those that want to be). And you will not have an L for 'loser' on yours because you are making them feel that way!"

Susie laughed. "Well, I'm glad to hear that."

"Consistency is the key, and the people on your database list will—just like your family— know if you are real or not. As they see you 'walk your talk' consistently, they will become believers, and Susie, your phone will start to ring regularly with referrals of clients from your database because you have a focused marketing plan which educates them to do it."

Philip relaxed. Susie, though, didn't put down her pencil until she was certain he was finished.

"The specifics of the way to do the rest is Principle #4, which I bet you're going to be learning this afternoon."

"That's right. With someone named Sara Simpson."

"Oh. Sara is a dynamo. Get ready to be bowled over. She'll have you learning about the Keep-InTouch program within minutes."

"Keep-InTouch—"

"That's right," Philip said. "But I'll let her tell you. You'll love it."

Susie finally put down her pencil.

Just then Highground walked in, and they both looked up, amazed that two hours had already passed.

"How is my star student?" he asked.

"She is going to be phenomenal," Philip said, getting to his feet.

"Are you leaving?" Susie asked Philip.

"Not far," he said, pointing to the table next to them.

Confused, Susie glanced at Highground.

He explained. "Susie, I'm going to take this seat here with you again. Philip, on the other hand, has a couple coming to meet him here in a few minutes. And he will sit down with them right next to us. That way, we can hear how he educates a new client without making the couple uncomfortable."

"Great idea," Susie agreed. "I like watching a master in action."

That made Philip grin. "This is a couple I've just started to work with, and I've asked them to come have a cup of coffee with me, because I want to explain the system to them. So this will really help you."

That's when he saw his couple come in, right on time. And he went to meet them.

For the next hour, Susie listened intently, amazed as Philip articulated all that he had shared with her that morning. She wished she'd brought a tape recorder.

For several minutes, as Philip and the couple ordered coffee and waited for it to arrive, they talked about the financial planning work he'd done for them. Then, to Susie's surprise and delight, they asked what the Highground pin he was wearing meant. Now Philip had the perfect opening. So he stated the philosophy of how he valued a lifetime relationship. And then, considering it was the perfect moment, he also presented to them a directory that was titled "In Touch with Friends and Associates." It had his company logo on it. Susie leaned too far over, trying to see this directory, which made the couple look at her. Quickly, she coughed and moved her chair around loudly working hard to be invisible again, which tickled Highground so much he had to muffle his own laughter. But he couldn't hide his pleasure at her enthusiasm.

"What is this directory?" she whispered to Highground. "That's a great idea!"

"You can do it, too. In fact, you should. It's all your own favorites, your tried-and-true businesses, dry cleaners, convenience stores, restaurants, the very establishments you tell people about all the time. Philip just got smart and printed up his own to give away. Listen to how he explains it," Highground whispered.

"This is an in-depth listing of all the businesses and services that I can personally recommend in the community," Philip was saying.

Susie wondered if Chuck's California Coffee Shop and Bistro, and Sheila Marie Deveroux Realty and Paul's company were all in there. Then she knew, of course, they were.

And this was the moment that Philip started explaining his High Ground Principles of Business. When he stated that he didn't spend any of his time or money in marketing to the general public, that he spends his energies on those that he serves by bringing them items of value on a regular basis, she started taking a new set of notes as quickly as she could.

And she wrote even faster, trying to capture his exact speech, especially when he said that if there were any way his staff could be of service: "Just Let Us Know."

"You know I mean this," Philip reminded them, since he'd already shown his excellence in the work he'd done for them. "The only thing I ask you is if you happen to know of any friends or associates that could use my services, Just Let Me Know, and I'll treat them just as I have treated you. This is the way I do business."

Susie gave up. She couldn't write that fast, and this was too good to miss by worrying about getting it all down. She just listened.

And that's when he looked confidently at the couple and said, "You see, the reason you came to me in the first place was because our mutually good friend had referred us, remember?"

The couple nodded.

"So I'm dedicated, as you can tell, to upholding the trust that has led us together."

"We appreciate that, too," the couple chimed in. "In fact, we do have some friends, the Johnsons, who could use your help. We'll make a point of calling them tonight for you. Just let us write their number down for you."

At this point, Highground motioned to Susie that they needed to leave. So Susie and Highground left the coffee shop and started walking down to the dock near where they had eaten lunch yesterday.

And he stopped by the same bench Susie sat on to start her 250x250 list. So much had happened since then, it felt like much longer than just yesterday, Susie suddenly thought.

"I believe this spot worked for you yesterday, Susie," Highground was saying. "What I would like you to do is take another 20 minutes or so and write out another step in your goals that you started yesterday—Goal #3. Okay, remember how to do this? Here's a new tape to listen to. Project yourself eight weeks into the future this time. I'll bring you a salad and let you enjoy the quiet for a bit."

The morning fog had given way to a lovely noon sun that set off the brilliant blue ocean, the one that always confirmed why she had moved here in the first place. She sat down, pulled out her notebook, turned to the third goal's page and began to write:

GOAL #3

GOAL: *Professionally brand my own style with this system, then begin a proactive education system in all that I say and do with all those I know.*

Goal Date: *8 weeks from today*

The date is *Aug. 1* **and I have:** *everything available for this system in place. From the communication on my business cards, stationery and fax form, to additional hand outs that match up with me and my new philosophy. Because I have worked hard to incorporate this system with my style, I now feel comfortable telling people that I work mainly by referral. I have actual proof of action all around me. I am educating everyone on a daily basis how I can help them and how they can help me. It is truly a win/win scenario.*

I have already experienced: *ongoing positive response from my clients and all that I come into contact with. I am amazed at the people, many of whom I once thought to have real control of their businesses, wanting to know how I have set all of this up.*

I feel: *more of myself. For the first time in my life, I feel genuine about myself because I now have the freedom or license to be me. I love my products and what they do for others and feel I can competently share them with others in a way that can work for them.*

I am excited about: *helping others get involved in my business and showing them how they can be themselves, too. I really am excited about giving them the new-found freedom that Highground has shown me.*

My associates and colleagues are: *impressed with my professional branding of my new system. Many have asked me to share with the people they work with my experience and how I have achieved it.*

I am determined to: *surround myself with the right visual confirmations that I practice what I preach so I will be genuine in making this system really mine.*

The time flew. Before she knew it, Highground was tapping her on the shoulder, then sitting down beside her to read her new goal. When he finished, he said nothing, gave her a proud smile, then got up and beckoned her to follow him.

So, hurriedly pushing her notebook back into

her satchel, she stood up and did just that.

"Ready for Principle #4?" Highground asked, already knowing Susie's answer.

Chapter 6

IGHGROUND AND SUSIE LEFT THE OCEANFRONT
and walked up a few blocks from the dock
toward Rancho Benecia's downtown area.

As they walked, Highground said, "Well,
Susie, you're in the home stretch. Your insights
and goals you just wrote prove that you continue
to show that you are an amazingly quick study.
Before we take this next stop to learn the last
principle, what specific insights do you have?
Anything you want to talk about?"

Susie hesitated, not quite sure she wanted to
share her deepest fear with him. He'd now
become a sort of mentor to her, and she didn't
want to disappoint him. But he had asked, so she
told him.

"Mr. Highground, you obviously have helped
a number of people through this process. And all
you say is continuing to unfold in a logical man-

95

ner. But I guess my biggest hurdle or anxiety is how quickly will I see results? I guess I'm a bit afraid of failure again. I know it should work, but will it really work for me?"

"I appreciate your candor, Susie. You have to be honest with me and with yourself. But believe me—it will work, as long as you trust the process. That is why the first three questions I asked you when we first met were so important. Remember them?"

She nodded. "Am I comfortable with myself, do I believe in my products, and can I stay the course."

"That's right. You are comfortable enough with yourself, you definitely believe in your company's products, and I believe after this next meeting it will all come together for you how to 'stay the course,' to 'trust the system.' So," he said, stopping in the middle of the block, "are you ready to meet the dynamic Business/Business Sara Simpson, president of Simpson Systems?"

Susie looked behind her and there was a large, renovated warehouse with a sign hung over its big, artistic, metal doors announcing "Simpson Systems." Susie's eyebrows popped high at the very expensive look of it all. But then she nodded.

Highground opened the doors for her. "Now, remember. Sara is 'Business/Business.' She is very high-principled or she couldn't run our system so successfully, but she is the daughter of one of the area's first big business owners and she wants to be known for being her father's daughter—and then some, I can tell you that. She proves, though, that this system works for anyone once they realize the kind of person they are and are happy to embrace it. Okay, here we go."

They entered the elegantly-appointed waiting area with its globe of the world smartly blended into the Simpson Systems logo hanging from the high ceiling.

Highground didn't slow, though. He walked straight to the elevator, guiding Susie along with him, stepped inside, and hit the top floor's button.

In a moment, the doors swooshed open to the executive floor. They passed the two secretaries who seemed to know Highground by sight, and without a word were escorted into the private conference room of the corner office with the best view of the harbor at Rancho Benicia overlooking the Baha Mier Cliffs.

This was the "war" room of Sara Simpson. Highground and Susie had not been there a minute when Sara strode into the room—high heels clicking and expensively-tailored suit swaying like silk with her every move. She exuded the confidence of any Fortune 500 executive and grinned widely as soon as soon as she laid eyes on Highground.

"David Michael Highground, where have

you been? You disappear then reappear at the strangest of times. I was just asking Chuck about you. This must be Susan McCumber, the lady you have spoken so highly of. How do you do, Susan?" she stretched out her hand.

For a moment, Susie thought she just might stay a more formal and sophisticated "Susan" for this very successful contemporary of hers. But then she remembered that she liked herself just fine. She took her hand and shook it solidly.

"My pleasure," she said to Sara. "And please call me Susie."

Then Sara, all business and proud of it, was off and running. She marched them over to the corner of the polished oval table and waved them a command to sit, and she was talking, her total focus on Susie:

"Susie, David has given me an extensive background on you. And what I would like to do for you in the next 2 1/2 hours is give you an in-depth look at our Keep-InTouch program, how it works for us, its results and how it can work for you. Before I do, I would like to give you an idea of where I was before I instituted this program."

The agenda was set. In the few minutes of the introduction and ensuing conversation, Susie understood exactly what a Business/Business person was like.

"Sounds like an excellent plan, Sara," Susie said, with all her business-like enthusiasm. She was suddenly very interested in how someone who obviously is so business-driven actually develops relationships. And it looked as if she may just find out.

"I took over this business at 23," Sara was saying in her clipped-speech way, as she leaned back in her black leather chair, "—when my father died. I was driven for a number of reasons—the loss I felt, the want to succeed, the need to help out my mother—but mostly I just wanted to prove to the world that Sam Simpson's daughter was able to make it on her own. I did the 'wall to wall' days, and gathered all my identity out of the business. I became obsessed with it. I drove people in my employ to the brink. I looked at customers as widgets, something that either was a good business decision or not. If they didn't match up with the numbers, they didn't hear from me. My sales people were the highest paid in the industry, but I drove them until they dropped. Oh, my volume continued to soar, and I received all the industry accolades which invigorated me more. Although my volume increased, the margins were tight, because that's the type of clients I ended up with—the shoppers. There was no loyalty."

She glanced at Highground. "I came to a great crossroads in my business five years ago. That's when I met David Michael Highground. I was referred to him from my father's best friend. He had come all the way from New York to visit my family and see me. My dad's friend knew him from childhood and loved him like a brother. What he really was doing out here was checking up on me, because he was close to Dad and I reminded him so much of Dad. He really gave me some great insights of who my dad really was—from a business point of view."

She paused, crossing her legs, and running a hand along her skirt to straighten it, "You see, I found out why so many people helped me when I started. It was because of my dad's good name.

"Although he was tough as any successful person in business, when it came to helping people through a crisis, especially others in business, he would drop everything he was doing and make himself available. Highground had helped Dad a long time ago when I was young and my dad's friend thought I should meet him. And my life changed dramatically, as well as my business, which was my life, of course. So when he called and asked if I could spend a few hours with you, I couldn't wait for the opportunity—the opportunity to pass it along."

"I really appreciate the insight into your background, Sara," Susie said, meaning it. "Thanks for sharing it."

Sara sat up and leaned across the table. "Well, Susie, let's get down to business. You now understand the lifetime value of a client base, the power of 250x250, how to build and ABC your database and how to educate your staff, your circle of influence, your clients and friends and how to brand all of your communication. So let's talk about the part of the system that actually delivers on this promise of having people call you on a regular basis to do business with you. Principle #4. That's the 'Keep-InTouch program.'"

Susie scrambled to get her notebook open.

"Good," Sara said, smiling at the notebook. "I remember that notebook. It's your lifeline in the beginning. Don't forget that for a minute. Now. 'Keep-InTouch' is the on-going monthly communication that your client base and circle of influence receives each month consistently, that is branded with your new Highground principles. Talking in the language of your ABC'd list, your C's receive something of value every quarter, your B's receive something of value every other month, and your A's receive a monthly communication from you. This program is as powerful as any targeted marketing campaign on the street today because it is perpetual and builds a bank account with clients and associates that allows you to go without talking to them for six or seven months. Of course, your B's and C's are very impressed, because when you do call, they feel like you are talking to them every other week. It's fantastic."

"This morning I heard about 'Just Let Me Know'," Susie volunteered.

"Wonderful. That is as genuine as it sounds, too. When you actually show consistency with this, you will never feel awkward about saying to anyone: 'Just let me know if I can help you in any way. And if you have any friends or associates who could use my services, please give me their names. And I promise to treat them as well as I've treated you.' Now, if they have not heard from you recently or done business with you lately, that might sound self-serving. But what you'll find is when you send items along every month that are directed at building the relationship, and you have gone out of your way to help them, then you don't come across self-serving, and your call is always taken. And best of all, people do give you their friends' names. Why? Because they trust you. This program can even knock the edges off a tough businesswoman like me, and because of the professionalism shown in the program, I can demonstrate that I care. And I do, but in my own way."

"That's quite a testimony," Susie said.

"But you know what? In the end, it's not only good for me, but the program was the best decision for the business, time-wise, too, because I don't have to recreate the wheel every month for new clients. The old ones keep looking for ways to do business with us and our A's are a huge sales force for us because they are our biggest advocates. Having them tell the world (literally) about us is like having a free review written about your restaurant in The New York Times Entertainment Section as opposed to taking out a very expensive newspaper advertisement. Make sense?"

"Absolutely," Susie said. "But that's fine for a big operation like yours. How do I do it myself? How does someone like me decide what to send every month?"

Sara thought a moment. "That's a great question. Let me share something with you. When you are a sales organization like ours, you regularly outgrow your infrastructure. That means we often get so busy trying to deliver on our promises that we don't have time to send out everything we should. That's what that old saying means—the one that says every time a business grows by 40%, the infrastructure is shot. But here's the new twist for you: It holds true for a company like ours with 300 employees and also yours with one employee.

"So, what's the answer? The answer is that the program needs to be laid out like any good marketing program—one year in advance. Other than special gifts and recognition for your A's, you already know the holidays, events, that sort of thing, right?"

"Right."

"When you can focus on this for one short period of time and have the whole program focused, it is absolutely awesome in its results.

We definitely send out our program, but we always contract out all the new materials each year. A friend of our friend Mr. Highground here handles it for us. As a matter of fact, they did everything for us the first three years."

Susie looked at Highground. "You mean, you can have this all set up for me?"

Highground nodded. "If you want. You can personalize them anyway you need to for your own business."

With that, Sara hoisted up two beautifully-crafted posters with the logo "Keep-InTouch" emblazoned on the front. They both showed 12

Principle #4: "The power of a Keep-InTouch program"

months of a particular item and when it would be sent. Susie looked closely at the greeting cards.

"Our sales people have a presentation that talks about the lifetime value we place on each client and our Keep-InTouch program of communication," Sara continued. "Then we follow up, with material such as these, and the results are history. We're Number One in our field."

Susie saw a cross-section of all the different types of material sent to their ABC database list which included magazines on family with their business name on it, holiday cards, Valentine's Day cards, Christmas in July cards and on and on, all planned, all beautifully produced. "But these seem so corporate in design," Susie had to say.

Sara laughed. "What do you expect from a Business/Business person like me? Fortunately, David Michael's friend designs products for the relational side as well as the business side of personalities he deals with. You have to figure out who you are, be true to that, and select your designs around that."

Susie turned to Highground. "Do I have to go through your friend? Not that I wouldn't want to, but if I didn't want to...?"

Highground began to answer but Sara raised a well-manicured hand. "Our Mr. Highground gives input to everything his printer friend produces. If you want to do the Keep-InTouch program yourself, you certainly can, but frankly—forgive my directness— it would be foolish to do that. It's much more efficient simply to select the right line for you, have your name put on the brand, drop your database off to Highground's buddy and let him do it, so you concentrate on what you do best. Highground knows the system better than anyone. Make sense?"

"Yes, it actually does."

"And with the simple 12 month program in place—and it changes every year—you can concentrate on your A's. You can make all sorts of choices for them—special items of value and appreciation to send them for a referral, help in your business, something to commemorate their special events and so on. The program handles all of that. The results of something consistently showing up at your client's door, and the thought that every new contact you have gets included in this concept, is so satisfying that everyone you now meet is in play for your business. When I look at our reports on business coming out of our data-base, it's absolutely mind-blowing! The average increase in business per client because of the trust built into the relationship, and the minuscule cost of finding a new client because of the resulting referrals, as opposed to what we used to spend on marketing, is incredible." She sat back in her chair and held up her hands in amazement.

"Sounds like you're happy," Susie said, smiling at her enthusiasm.

"Let me put it this way. We used to 'hunt' those clients with a shotgun. Now we are using a rifle with the best scope on the market."

"Spoken like a true Business/Business!" Highground chimed in with a laugh. "Let's go introduce Susie to your sales staff and see how this works. What do you say?"

Sara got to her feet and so did Highground and Susie. "As a matter of fact," Sara said, already headed for the door, "we are just beginning a sales meeting for some new recruits. Our manager is explaining what 'Just Let Me Know' means and how we introduce the Keep-InTouch program, so let's go."

When they walked into the training room, everyone noticed them. Sara gave them a little go-on wave as she seated Highground and Susie and sat down beside them.

The manager was just starting. He gave an overview of the company's commitment to their lifetime clients. He ran a video of a successful national airlines commercial that showed a company president telling his sales force that they had just lost their largest and oldest account because they quit the personal touch that had gotten them the clients in the first place. Then it showed him giving out airline tickets to their sales people with the command that they were going to "retouch" all they had served in person. And when one of the people asked the company president where

107

he was going, he simply said he was going to see an old friend, referring to the account they had lost.

As the commercial ended, the manager stated that this is the situation their competition is in, losing their clients over the lack of personal touch. And this is a situation the Simpson Systems will never be because of a program called "Keep-InTouch."

"We have a statement that is almost our slogan," the manager explained. It's 'Just Let Me Know.' And that means if we can help our client in anyway—any way at all—we are available at all times. The late founder of this company, Sam Simpson, was always available and our current President Sara is determined to carry on that tradition, not only in words but in action. The next part of that directive is easy, asking them to refer their friends and associates with the promise that we will treat them as we well as they were treated." He paused, and leaned over the podium. "Of course, if you don't treat them that well, the statement will backfire." They all shared a laugh.

He went on to reiterate the Keep-InTouch program, and what Susie heard was exactly what Sara had just taught her. And by the time they left, Susie had put the finishing touches on the notes she'd been taking all day long.

As they left the meeting, Susie felt a new sense of confidence. She looked directly into Sara's eyes and thanked her for her time.

"Susie," Sara said, shaking her hand, "in the event things change and you consider the computer field, give me a call. Otherwise, if I can help you in any way.... 'Just Let Me Know!'" And with a broad smile, she turned on her high heels and went back to work.

And as Susie and Highground left the building, Susie had no doubt Sara Simpson meant every word.

"Wow," Susie said to Highground.

Highground smiled. "As I said at the beginning, Sara Simpson proves that the system works for anyone who has the heart for it, no matter what their personal style might be."

"That's the truth," Susie agreed.

"Well, it's late," Highground said, checking his watch.

"But I've learned so much!" Susie said, a little unwilling to let her new mentor go so quickly.

"Data dump," Highground agreed. "In fact, you may have learned too much for one day, not to mention two."

"Oh, I don't think so," Susie said with a laugh. "I am revved."

That made Highground laugh out loud. "I can see that! And I love it. But this is what I want you to do to let everything simmer, to let you think about this last principle and how it affects all the rest—I want you to go home and fill in your last goal sheet. And then I want you to review everything in your notebook, making notes to yourself on every point, filling up every blank place with simple, achievable goals and with ideas and questions. Then I'll meet you tomorrow morning at 8 a.m. sharp and we will look everything over."

"And then what?"

"And then you begin a whole new chapter in your life," Highground said with a twinkle in his eye. He waved, and hurried away, in his disappearing way.

Susie stood there a moment, watching where he had vanished, and she could see the waterfront ahead. And beyond that, she could see the water, and the horizon. The sun was going down, dusk was falling, but for some reason, she felt like something was dawning in her life, something new. And it felt good.

She rushed home, made dinner, and sat down at her table to fill out the last goal sheet:

GOAL #4

GOAL: *The next 12 months of my Keep-InTouch program is in place.*

Goal Date: *12 weeks from today*

The date is *Oct. 1* **and I have:** *laid out my next 12 months of my Keep-InTouch program. I have selected the 12 communications that best* *match my style to be delivered each month. The pre-written communications are in place and the items of value are already ordered. Or I have the telephone numbers in my planner with the dates listed in advance ready to be made. I have a small example of each in my portfolio to show those interested in my business how my system works.*

I have already experienced: *so much positive response and business through my system that it's hard to believe the hopelessness I felt only months before because I did not have a plan of action that suited me.*

I feel: *proud of the hard work I have done and the discipline I have shown to execute this program so well. I feel a sense of accomplishment because of the completion as well as the business I have experienced.*

I am excited about: *the prospect of hiring an assistant to help with administering the system while I spend my time helping other people with my products.*

My associates and colleagues are: *blown away by the completeness of the system I have in place and the success it is producing. I, on the other hand, am happy that I can be genuinely me and not have to live up to something I am not.*

I am determined to: *continue with this program and deliver it consistently so I may concentrate on the things I like to do—help other*

111

people reach their goals in life, too.

❖ ❖ ❖ ❖

Susie sat back, laid her pen down, and looked
at her last goal. Then she flipped back to the
beginning of her notebook to scan the other three
goals, along with the principles, and her eyes land-
ed on her first hastily jotted attempt at her 250x250
list. *Principle #1*, she automatically thought: The
250x250 Rule—It's not only who you know that
counts, it's who your clients know. There were
over 160 names on it. She looked them over one
by one, getting more excited with each name.
And she began to automatically ABC them all,
jotting down the appropriate letter by each name,
checking the ones she'd tried the first day for practice to see if she still agreed with her "rankings."

Principle #2, she thought with a smile: Create a
database and ABC it. Now she could see how the
list worked. In fact, she was actually looking forward to having this great reason to re-connect with
some of these old, familiar names.

"*Principle #3:* Just Let Me Know—Educate your
clients through what you say and what you send
consistently," she quoted proudly to herself.

"And *Principle #4*: The power of a 'Keep-
InTouch' program..."

Interesting, she thought, shaking her head.
She remembered all Four Principles of the

system—The High Ground System of Business—easily. The best part, though, was that she could see how the whole plan worked, all right here before her. It was truly simple, with amazingly deep, ongoing results.

She closed the notebook and rested her hand on it. "Oh my," she mumbled, grinning to herself. "I'm going to have a hard time sleeping tonight."

And she was exactly right.

Chapter 7

THE NEXT MORNING, SUSIE WOKE FAR TOO EARLY
again. So she got dressed, grabbed her notebook, and took the long way to Chuck's cafe,
savoring this new feeling and this moment in her
life. It still felt like a beginning. And it felt good.

At 8 a.m., she walked into the cafe. And there
was Highground chatting with Chuck behind the
counter. They both greeted her with big smiles,
and Highground strolled over, waving her to a
table up front where they could see the water.

"So, how are you doing this morning?"
Highground wanted to know as they sat down.

"Oh, Mr. Highground. Great. Just great."

That pleased Highground tremendously. "I
can see the transformation happening before my
eyes. You are hardly the same woman I met three
days ago."

"Thanks to you."

"No," Highground corrected her. "No matter

115

how much knowledge you gain about the system, it only works if you stay true to the three questions I asked you. And I think you will."

"That's my plan."

"Let's get out your notebook."

Susie zipped out the notebook and plopped it open to the Goal #4 page she filled in last night.

Highground examined it and nodded approvingly, patting the notebook. "Susie, what I'd like for us to do this morning is to review all you've experienced the last couple of days, and then talk about your plans for the future—your newfound plan of action. Okay?"

Susie sighed. "I have to tell you, Mr. Highground, Philip called you a perception-changer, and that is exactly what you are. You change perceptions which change attitudes. I have often told people to cheer up or look at the bright side of things, but there's no way to do that when we are dodging falling trees, as you put it. A person's attitude can only change when his or her perception changes and that's what you, along with your friends, have done for me the past couple of days. For that I am deeply appreciative."

That seemed to please him deeply. "Thank you," he said. "But, as I said, it's really up to you now."

"But now I know the combination!" Susie said, pointing to the notebook page before them. It was the "Right Combination for Success" lock drawing of Principle #4 that showed all four principles and the lock popped open. "You know, I smiled when I saw that last lock open on Principle #4 the very first day you gave me the notebook, even before I knew about the power of a Keep-InTouch program. Now it makes me smile even bigger."

Highground cocked his head at the picture and smiled, too. "The combination can unlock a whole new world." Highground flipped back to her goal sheets. "And from the looks of these goals, you're halfway there. You have projected yourself into the future several weeks for each goal and done it admirably. And your tasks are simple and achievable, which makes each goal reasonably attainable. Good for you. My bet is you'll attain them."

That made Susie beam.

"You know where I'd like us to start?" he suddenly decided. "Why don't you explain to me where you were two days ago and where you are right now."

Susie laughed. "Do you realize I almost didn't call you because I was concerned about my cellular phone bill? That's where I was. My biggest frustration was that I had no direction in who I talked to about my business and what to do with them after I made contact with them. I was either coming on too strong or I simply couldn't connect with them at all, so how could

I develop a relationship?

"I thought I needed some grandiose marketing or advertising plan that would save me. I was continually looking toward tomorrow and hoping the perfect plan would just appear. When it didn't, I hit the wall and that's when we met. You know," she realized, "strangely enough, what I had been hoping for did appear—when Chuck referred me to you."

That's when Chuck appeared at her elbow carrying her usual hazelnut with steamed milk and a biscotti, just like the one he pushed toward her three days earlier to coax her into telling him her problems. He pushed it—ceremoniously—across the table toward her.

Susie loved it, laughing out loud.

"It's amazing what 72 hours can do for a person, isn't it?" Chuck said, patting Highground on the shoulder, before going back to his work.

"How long ago did he begin your system?" Susie asked Highground, gazing appreciatively back Chuck's way.

"About five years ago," answered Highground. "And it may not surprise you to know that he was referred to me by a friend of his, too."

"No, that doesn't surprise me at all. Now." She dunked her biscotti into her coffee and took a big bite out of it.

"So go on. You left off at the point Chuck referred me, I believe."

"Well, you know what happened after that. Now I have a proactive plan that fits me. I don't feel the need to try to imitate someone else. I understand and appreciate the old saying that it's 11 times more expensive to find a client than to keep an existing one. My problem was I didn't have a system in place to keep my existing clients by communicating with them regularly enough, let alone ask them for referrals. But I now have your system, the High Ground System, that can demonstrate my consistency and earn the right to ask and receive, hopefully, referrals from my special people."

"As soon as you begin to live it, Susie, it is your system. The success of 'staying the course.'"

"And I'll be proud to claim it. Because it seems to me that the beauty of this system, especially the Keep-InTouch program, is the way it communicates. So many people talk about communicating with their database, but few do, other than the occasional mailer trying to sell something else or brag about themselves. But I truly believe that when I tell my client, 'Just Let Me Know' if I can help them, I will be prepared to. And then when I ask if they have any friends or associates that could use my services, and promise to treat them as I have treated the client, it will mean something. Because I've proved myself through consistency, right? Through 'staying the course' by 'staying in touch'."

119

Highground sat back and shook his head. "That is such a nice way of putting it." He looked proudly at his new student. "It's obvious you have come into your own now, Susie. This is always such a high point for me."

But Susie wasn't finished. "You know, before I met you, if someone gave me a card, I put it in a file and never did a follow-up. When I finally got around to calling them about something I was offering, so much time had passed since the last time I'd made contact with them, I felt like a fake, a counterfeit, calling and acting as if I were interested in the relationship. But both of us knew the only reason I was truly calling. I was acting like an opportunist and the way that made me feel was what was holding me back. My stomach kept turning. I know that now."

Susie smiled. "But everything is going to change. Now, I will be doing things the old-fashioned way—I will earn the right to ask for a referral. I understand these great principles and how they apply to business, I will be in touch with the people in my life on a regular basis and I now know how to actually do that, communicating with them and consistently offering them items of value. And I have a sneaky feeling that many of them will be impressed for the sole reason that they have always wanted to do this kind of communication themselves but never knew exactly how."

Highground lifted his coffee cup in a toast to

Susie. So Susie lifted hers, too. "You should be proud of yourself, Susie. I salute you."

"Thank you," Susie said, and clinked her coffee cup with his, then dunked the last of her biscotti and popped it in her mouth. "You can't imagine how proud I am of myself. But I'll be more proud once this whole system is up and rolling and I'm living it everyday."

"Exactly. You have an excellent grasp of the system. Now I encourage you to stay the course for four months. Work at it, Susie. Do it. Because if you do, you will settle into a routine that will be uniquely you."

Then Highground placed a piece of paper on Susie's notebook. "Put this into your notebook. It's what I call my 'Help List,' a listing of people and resources to help you put the system to work for you. You'll find everything available to you listed there—from a Keep-InTouch newsletter to thank you cards with 'Just Let Me Know' printed on the inside to a person who will actually help you send out items each month to your database, if you need the extra pair of hands. They all are there to help, to make the system work as it should for you.

"Use them or do it yourself; just stay the course, and set it into motion. Just remember, once you have demonstrated consistency with clients you already have relationships with, you will never have competition again. You own the

121

relationship in the wonderful way that you can claim a friend."

Susie looked excitedly at the Help List, and began to make notations on it, thinking ahead to when she could get started on everything.

That's when she noticed that Highground had stood up. "You are going to do great, Susie. It's been a pleasure getting to know you," he was saying. "If I can help you in any way at all, just let me know. And if you have any friends who can use my help, just let me know that, too."

"Do you have to leave?" Susie said, suddenly rather sad.

"See you, old friend!" she heard Chuck call from behind her. She looked around at Chuck, and when she turned back, the mysterious Mr. Highground had disappeared yet again.

She could only shake her head and smile after him. Chuck walked up and began picking up their dirty dishes. "Quite a guy, huh."

Susie could only shake her head again. She picked up her notebook and the Help List Highground had given her, then got to her feet, too. And with a big smile for Chuck, she said, "You know, the day is young, and I'm ready to get going. See you later, Chuck."

Chuck watched Susie leave with a confidence in her step that was missing a few days ago. "The high ground will do that for you," he murmured, picking up the last of their dishes, and feeling a

deep sense of satisfaction at his role in the drama of "Susie McCumber's professional transformation," he thought to himself, enjoying the sound of it. He liked Susie, and he had no doubt the "high ground" was for her.

Besides, he realized with a happy smile as he headed back behind his antique oak counter, it didn't hurt that even though there were other coffee places in town, there would be only one that Susie McCumber would continue to frequent, not to mention tell all her friends and clients about—and that was California Coffee Cafe and Bistro.

Chapter 8

S IX MONTHS LATER

It was another perfect morning at the California Coffee & Bistro as the regulars, including Susie McCumber, lined up for the morning cups of the "usual" before starting their day.

The phone behind the antique oak bar rang and Chuck, in the middle of a double cappuccino, no whip, stopped, grabbed it, talked a second, then turned and looked at Susie, and said, "It's for you."

Susie frowned, confused. After all, she hadn't had her coffee yet. "Who is it?"

Chuck handed her the phone and returned to his coffee creation. "A friend of yours."

"Hello?" Susie said tentatively into the receiver.

"Susie! Highground here. How are you? It's been six months."

That woke her up. "I'm just great, Mr. Highground. How are you? I've loved getting your postcards from all over. You've been on the move."

"Just helping out a few friends," came his response. "I'm back in town now. And I've been hearing good things about you. I just want to thank you for keeping your promise about 'staying the course.' It sounds as if you are doing fabulously and I'm really happy for you."

"Oh, thank you," Susie purred. "It has been fabulous. Absolutely! I can't wait to tell you the whole story."

"Well, I can't wait to hear it. Which brings me to why I called. I do have a favor to ask of you."

"Anything."

"I have a new friend that needs some help and I wanted to know if you could meet us tomorrow and...."

"Talk about one of the principles and share where I was and where I am now? You bet. It would be my utter pleasure. I'll be here."

Susie handed the phone back to Chuck with one hand and took her hazelnut with steamed milk from him with the other.

"Everything okay?" he asked, hanging up the phone.

"Better than okay," she answered with a

grateful shake of head. "And all because of you."

Susie took a few steps away, then stopped, turned back to Chuck and said:

"You know something, Chuck? He really was the Referral of a Lifetime."

Use Our *Free*
Book Study
and **Leader's Guide**

We encourage you to share this system with your organization. Typically, you retain only 10% of what you read, but you learn 95% of what you teach. By teaching this material to others you will help them gain the tools to develop a successful business based on relationships, while deepening your own understanding of these principles. In turn, by participating with you, they will grasp how to teach this material to others in their team. You offer a valuable service which can be duplicated to build their business.

Meet for coffee or talk over a conference call. Book Study and Leader's Guides are available free to readers of this book at our web-site, "www.keep-intouch.com", or by fax on demand at 1-800-638-8340.

keep-IN Touch.com